Passion Jardins
Selections

Ideas for Better Gardening

Height	Diameter	Bloom	Sun	Partial Shade	Shade	Hardiness Zone	Scent	Bird	Butterfly	Deer

Proven Value: Resistant, dependable, easy to grow plants.

Plants with very special traits: "must haves" for the garden.

Newly introductions well worth trying.

Passion Jardins Merchants:
A Growing Passion for Gardening!

Yet again this season, our stores are places where choice and quality mix perfectly. In an instant you can discover a wide range of products developed with passion by people with experience, all to your great satisfaction.

Without any doubt, the experts from Passion Jardins know better than anyone how to inspire you. They have just what you need to know to create your own outdoor universe. For them, the garden is an inexhaustible field of experiences that titillate all the senses: smell, taste, touch, hearing, and sight – while bringing bits of poetry to the gardener's imagination. Their greatest pleasure comes from stimulating the creativity of home gardeners and helping them, through their suggestions, to develop a magnificent garden around their home.

Like you, Passion Jardins experts are seriously passionate about gardening! By visiting one of the network's 36 garden centres, you quickly understand why our motto is 'A Growing Passion for Gardening'.

Inspirational Suggestions

At Passion Jardins, it's easy to profit from the staff's generous advice. All the employees are trained to help you, notably in mixing and matching your plants so you can create a unique décor that will be the envy of the neighbourhood.

In all our employees, the passion for gardening is palpable. You'll see, they be able to inspire all your gardening projects by telling you all about the latest trends in new plants or by showing you decorative elements that will add a note of originality to your garden.

People Who Respect Nature

These days, it is important to respect nature in all aspects of our life, including gardening activities. The specialists at Passion Jardins understand the importance of the environment and favour products that respect nature because they ensure a top performance in plants. For example, Sunburst Quality soils, fertilizers, mulches, and lawn seeds, which are exclusive to Passion Jardins, will make sure your plants meet your every expectation, that is, plants that bloom abundantly and in brilliant colours!

Thanks to Passion Jardins experts, you'll discover all the pleasures of gardening. By learning to love what nature offers us, we can become closer to nature… and that's exactly how your merchant helps you garden by offering this guide prepared with passion by our team of experts.

Dear client,

It's with great pleasure that we present the first edition of Passion Jardins Selections: Ideas for Better Gardening.

Created by professionals and passionate gardeners in the horticultural industry, this new tool was developed to adequately meet the needs expressed by many among you who, above all, are looking for clear and simple answers to their questions. As you read through the pages, you'll learn to better enjoy and understand you garden so it can be transformed into the garden of your dreams. You'll also discover a multitude of plants, including some great discoveries, some tried-and-true favourites and, of course, lots of new introductions. You'll appreciate their photos and you'll familiarize yourself with how to grow them thanks to descriptive texts that tell all about their general needs.

Not only that, but you'll quickly discover that most of the tips and tricks found in the section "Green Thumb Tips" respect the environment while at the same time making gardening activities easier.

In short, lots of inspirational ideas are waiting for you in this new guide that will soon become your garden companion.

Have a great gardening season!

Your Passion Jardins Merchant.

Satisfaction Guaranteed:
helping you achieve gardening success

To help ensure that your efforts will be crowned with success, Passion Jardins offers you their Satisfaction Warranty program. Buy Qualité Soleil transplanting soil or root-building fertilizer when you buy your seedlings or plants, and take advantage of our guarantee program.

Look for the Warranty logo on our selected products, read the conditions of the Warranty, and follow the recommendations of the Passion Jardins planting guide. It's the guaranteed and ideal way to grow a healthy garden!

At Passion Jardins, we take your **gardening success** to heart.

Ici, nous cultivons la Passion

passionjardins.com

Table of contents

Better Living
in Your Garden

*The secret
of creating
atmospheres,
of discovering
textures, and
of using the charm
of old-fashioned
perfumes…*

If there is a word that has more than its share of meanings, it is certainly "garden"!
The secret of creating atmospheres, of discovering textures, and of using the charm of old-fashioned perfumes will be presented here as will other methods of coming to grips with styles, new ideas in ecology, and appropriate plant choices. Yep! They are all part of gardening! All those themes, and many more will be within your reach so you can take full advantage of your own corner of paradise. Read on… and dream!

Understanding Nature

If nature doesn't normally leave much room for a surplus, it abhors a vacuum even more and fills one in rapidly.

We all know that nature is beautiful and when we are in harmony with nature, it always makes us feel good. Sometimes too, nature can seem far away and mysterious, even wild. It's probably the calmness of nature that touches us at first, then its diversity and freshness. Everything seems drowsy, yet… under a cover of calmness, nature encloses an entire world that works non-stop. For example, all the elements of a forest, from the tallest tree to the carpet of perennials that cover the soil to the soil insects and microorganisms, have their place and each plays a role that benefits the forest community. It's a bit like a small city where everyone puts their shoulder to the wheel.

The secret of a forest, or of any natural landscape, is that it tends towards balance… a precious balance that makes it possible for all its members to both evolve and survive. If nature doesn't normally leave much room for a surplus, it abhors a vacuum even more and fills one in rapidly. This is the famous "law of nature" and we can learn a lot from this system that both endures and evolves at the same time. With a bit of observation, we learn that tall trees protect smaller ones, that shrubs offer food and refuge to small wildlife, and that leaf litter, that is the layer of dead leaves on the ground that is in eternal decomposition, is just as important for the forest environment as are all living elements. That's what we call an ecosystem. This organization, which becomes more and more honed over time, teaches us useful lessons that we can easily transpose to the garden.

First, in order to welcome as much life as possible, like birds and butterflies, you have to diversify the plant groups, including trees, shrubs, and perennials. In fact, the easiest way to copy nature is to take a keen interest in diversity. A garden mostly made up of perennials, for example, will never be balanced. Even if a garden may not look like a forest, it is nevertheless made up of living beings that instinctively work towards balance. Since we're the ones who set up gardens, it is also up to us to help our plants find the ideal place to grow, according to their needs. When they're in a state of balance, plants are in better health, need much less care from us, and are not as bothered by insects because birds eat the insects… and the birds are there because we've planted trees for their shelter. It's a chain in which each link has its own strength and our role as gardeners is to find the right place for each plant. No matter what natural environment we study, be it a mountain, a riverside, or a field, we discover that each one is balanced. Each plant that grows and develops there can do so because it is in the right place. Transplanting it elsewhere, to a different environment, will automatically lead to its loss. The trees of the forest will never be the trees of the suburbs… But when a plant, nursery grown and newly introduced into your garden, responds well to its new home and can participate fully in the life of the new community (for example, by attracting bees to help pollinate other plants), it has found its ecological niche. In other words, the plant feels at home. And so it goes: a beautiful garden is a garden that, like nature, works in silence.

Harmonize Your Garden

*Creating
a landscape
is building
a reflexion
of ourselves.*

Designing is an art, the art of bringing disparate elements together. On the one hand, there is the idea you want to express, the result you so dearly desire, and on the other, there is the "main dish", the final result, made up of ingredients you must carefully choose and mix in order to create a harmonious, tasteful blend. In other words, it's just like fine cooking! To design a landscape, you have to have an overall view and a solid base to build on… a theme for example. Without a goal, the design simply runs in circles, getting nowhere. You then have to choose the right ingredients, look for quality and calculate quantities, again as in a recipe. The choice of ingredients can make all the difference between a tasty dish and an insipid stew… and between a "disparate series of plantings" and a "landscape".

When you design a landscape in which you'll be living every day, you first have to understand the space itself: the amount of light, the type of soil, the direction of the winds, etc. But landscape design also involves, above all, letting it evolve,

comes into play. To successfully structure the landscape, you need to give it a base, just like a soup, something you can build upon... and that's what trees and large shrubs do ever so well. In fact, they are essential ingredients without which you

because nature is alive and constantly changes, just like people do. The structure of a home landscape is made up of a lot, a house, and of the people who inhabit the two. You have to frame this space, give it meaning and place and that's where the idea of "creative cooking" with plants

can never create a proper balance! In the case of trees, notably in urban and suburban settings where space is limited, it is best to choose specimens of small to medium height and to plant two or three than to plant a single tall one that will take years to fill in. As for large shrubs, like common lilacs, they'll help to re-establish harmony through their visual presence. This base of trees and large shrubs should make up at least half of the landscape. Next you need something to "thicken the soup", to link together the individual ingredients you've already brought together. That's the job of small and medium-size shrubs as well as dwarf conifers (the creeping types are ideal).

Grouped together in a mass planting, they'll be the thickener that ties the different flavours together… so be generous, we're not on a diet here! Now we need to finish our recipe with spices… and that's where perennials, bulbs, and

annuals come in. Sprinkle them on the landscape for their delicate qualities, their colours, textures, and inherent beauty, and they'll help give your landscape recipe a unique flavour all its own!

Still Useful

Better Living in Your Garden

Recuperating, recycling and reusing give new life to water and to containers...

Over the last few years, recycling has become a daily habit. Municipalities have made the effort to return to factories materials they can transform and reintroduce on the market as something new. This good habit is helping to reduce considerably the quantities, unfortunately still important, of waste going to landfill sites.

Recycling is one way of participating in this community effort, but the good news is that there are others! Recovery is another form of recycling, one that is entirely to our advantage. Recovering rainwater in barrels or other containers, for example, reduces the amount of drinking water used in the garden, water that our municipalities spent a lot of money treating. Not only does using rainwater reduce waste, the water thus collected is actually better for plants, as several studies have shown.

First, rainwater is naturally warm, therefore doesn't cause a shock to plants when applied to leaves and roots, unlike water directly from the tap. Not only that, but the chemicals used to purify water and to make it potable are not always good for plants; they prefer good old-fashioned rainwater. After all, it's a natural product!

Of course, another obvious way of recovering is to produce compost. Even if a compost pile may seem a bit rustic, it's by far the best restaurant in town for your garden plants! All garden wastes, except branches and diseased leaves, can be added to the mix. Added to a growing mix and well moistened, these green wastes are turned into brown gold. Fall leaves chopped with the lawn mower, lawn clippings, faded flowers… in fact all these little bits of former living material will engender another form of life. This copies the way nature does its own recycling: the forest has had its own composting factory since the beginning of time. A few tools, a bit of space and the possibility of feeding your garden for free are factors to seriously consider. Inquire about composting techniques: they're very easy.

Now that we've looked at recovery, let's look at reusing, that is, using in a new way objects that, once they've been used, would otherwise have found themselves in the recycling bin or, worse yet, the garbage. What a sad option, especially when so many materials and containers could still be reused. The semi-rigid transparent food packages muffins and vegetables come in make perfect little greenhouses for seedlings. Dryer softener sheets, after use, can be placed at the bottom of pots to cover the drainage hole: excess water can flow through, but potting mix stays in place. Metal or plastic blinds, cut into strips, make excellent plant labels for the vegetable bed. And don't forget the plastic pots you bought your plants in can be used for transplanting, as weed baskets, and when you want to share bits of your garden with your friends, they're there again to help you. Once cleaned, they can also be used as storage cups for tools, string, stakes, etc. Why run to the store to buy more and more new products when you already have on hand objects ready to help you simplify life? Spend more time in the garden instead.

In the Light of Day

Playing with light means offering a vegetal parasol to give plants a bit of a break.

We always wait impatiently for the sun, but when it hits us with its full force, filling the garden with its rays, its brilliance makes us squint! This light, nearly white, is essential for plant growth, but some plants want lots of it and others less. A well-balanced garden should therefore take advantage of the effects of light.

A garden that is too sunny exhausts plants and their flowers always lose some of their sparkle. On the other hand, when shade is too dense, there is a lesser choice of plants and contrasts between light and shadow are too strong. Playing with light means offering a vegetal parasol to give plants a bit of a break. By carefully observing the sun's position you can, for example, painlessly integrate shrubs or small trees into a flower bed , as their foliage is light or divided into tiny leaflets and will filter the sun's rays. For backlighting, you can remove a few branches from mature trees so just enough light filters through to the ground. In doing so, choose

branches from the inside of the tree that are not too big and remove them one at a time, always checking to see the effect created. These two methods make it easy to discover the colours and textures of plants and let you introduce other plants into the mix.

That's when the magic occurs. As the sun travels through the sky, hues and contrasts change letting us admire the full richness of the landscape. Depending on the angle of the sun, you'll notice either the petals or the heart of a flower and these pieces become tiny lights glowing in the shade. As for foliage, it lets the light softly bring out its texture. Everything is in slow motion. Leaves reveal themselves; we clearly see each undulation, crack, and stripe. You could almost say that light has made an arrangement with its opposite, shade, to show us all the complexity of the leaves. It's a real little game of hide-and-seek.

Painters adore seeking these zones of light and shade that show us the garden from a new angle. After all, the impressionist painters of the 19th century, who painted outdoors, always sought the soft contrasts of light and shade. Where there is light or dense shade, another phenomenon becomes apparent: the look of colours themselves. Whites become more creamy and yellows let more green appear, forming the colour called chartreuse, magnificent in the shade. Yellow, whether from flowers or foliage, is always the best colour for shady spots, as are whites and creams. Because of their composition, these colours stand out from the crowd. When you create mass plantings with these hues, its like turning on a multitude of little lights!

Reds, on the other hand, fade away a bit in shade while pinks become more delicate. As for the blues in flowers, their intensity decreases. In the case of blue leaves, a greyish veil envelopes them… and that's why they are so beautiful! The intensity of light is alone responsible for the brilliance of natural colours. It's up to us to use them to highlight all the mysteries of the garden.

A Bit of Stability Leads to Greater Facility...

Think of ground-covers as living carpets, ready to do all the work for you!

When you have a large surface to cover, you usually think of confiding the job to a lawn, figuring it can go anywhere. However grass lawns, though they probably cover more "garden" than anything else on the planet, do have their limits when it comes to adapting to different environments. Shady, damp areas, or those that are in the dry shade of trees, or slopes that burn in the sun, those are all areas where lawns simply won't grow. There is no use trying to force a lawn to grow where it doesn't want to, it's better to look elsewhere! All the more so since the vegetable kingdom has numerous hidden treasures when it comes to covering bare ground.

Groundcovers are able to spread in all directions and cover the soil at a remarkable rate. Even so, there is no need to fear them spreading, all you have to do is to put in a barrier to stop them short. Among the dozens of groundcovers that are available, you'll always find one that you can grow in a difficult spot. It is worthwhile using them more than we do now, not only because they beautify our yards with their flowers and foliage, but because they don't need mowing and thus save us a lot of work. Slopes and embankments cause headaches for lawn owners, as they need constant watering. Due to the steep slope, water flows straight on by without sinking in, leaving lawn grasses dying of thirst. It's time to look for plants that are good at stabilizing embankments, plants that root quickly, that cover vast surfaces and, especially, that are not afraid of long

periods of drought. Several shrubs are ideal at this. Indeed, the environment of the forest floor can be an excellent inspiration for those seeking groundcovers. In a forest of towering trees, the soil is covered with a green carpet of various plants, plants that cool the air and conserve humidity. A groundcover also brings essential nutrients to the soil and often offers spring blooms. By introducing them into our flowerbeds, we can replace mulch that, though was a great help in the early years of the garden where it protected the soil and kept weeds down, isn't very colourful and needs to be replaced regularly. If you want to make gardening less of a struggle, there's one solution! Think of groundcovers not just as carpets of greenery and flowers, but as living carpets, ready to do all the work for you!

Discover Informal Hedges

Hedges are living structures that organize our outdoor space.

Canada is a vast country, but that is no reason why you can't hack out a little private space where you can feel at home! So why do we seem to believe that we must open your entire yard to all passers-by? What a shame to let others take advantage of what belongs to us, something that could become a beautiful private landscape only we can enjoy. The solution to this dilemma is simple and very pleasing: plant a hedge… but not just any hedge, an informal hedge.

A hedge, by definition, is a row of shrubs that delimits two spaces. But that doesn't mean that a hedge must necessarily be arborvitae (cedar) or that it can't move or change in variety and colour! Hedges are living structures that organize our outdoor space, such as the front and back yards, even as they improve the quality of that space.

They can do so many things that it is surprising we don't see more of them! Don't forget that hedges can gently enclose the front yard as well, giving it back to its owners. All you have to do is to choose a shrub, even a short one, and to plant it along the front limit of the lot. Instantly you'll find yourself at home! An informal hedge means that the shrubs it is composed of are grown without any formal pruning, letting their natural shape show. As for maintenance, only a minimum of

effort is required: pruning out damaged branches or, in certain cases, removing faded flowers. These simple treatments will ensure that, for example, a lilac hedge of unsurpassable perfume will bloom abundantly. What a show… and it repeats each month of May! Letting your hedges grow informally also means you can mix and match species and cultivars according to the plant's needs and your favourite colour schemes. Imagine, for example, a side yard dominated by two huge bare walls. To reduce their impact, you could start by planting a row of tall shrubs, like the highbush cranberry (*Viburnum trilobum*), stopping when the unattractive structural elements are no longer visible. Then extend the hedge forward with something shorter, like dwarf Korean lilac (*Syringa meyeri* 'Palibin') or *Weigela florida*. These plantings could then continue on, following the lot's outer limit or even wander over to a pathway. In that way, informal hedges create movement! By playing with heights, flowering seasons, and colours (and don't forget autumn leaves!), you'll find you have a

new landscape you can admire as much from your angle as passers-by can from the street! And choosing hedge plants is certainly easy enough: you'll find there is an impressive range of shrubs among which you'll find ones that can adapt to whatever light is available, the type of soil you have, and whatever height you're looking for. A hedge is a very important element in the structure of a landscape: it helps frame it and highlights your home's appearance. Your yard belongs to you, it's private property, and you have every right to frame the space and make it attractive and inhabitable. You'll even notice that, thanks to an informal hedge, relations with your neighbours will be greener and more floriferous than you would ever have imagined!

Everything Old is New Again

Our background as a gardening people may be modest, but when we stop to take a look...

Who doesn't have memories of the suave perfume of a freshly cut bouquet of lilacs or the enchanting fragrance of peonies overflowing from the path to Grandma's house? Canada may only have a short history of gardening, with memories that don't reach that far back, yet even so, the emotional charge that is attached to old-fashioned flowers always comforts us. All those old-fashioned plants, shared from mother to daughter, from one neighbour to another, are so familiar to us that we never consider that they probably come from a far-away land and not straight from the old homestead. We must continue to make sure these fragrances of lilacs, peonies, and roses continue to prosper, because history must go on.

While our gardener lineage may not go back all that far, there is one type of garden that has been part of our history since our ancestors first set foot in the New World and that's the vegetable bed. For our ancestors, it was often the only garden that they knew and it has marked our roots. A vegetable bed recalls centuries of tough living; it ensured the survival of generation after generation! In today's world vegetable gardening has become a pleasurable activity for many,

yet others always seem surprised to see people in sunhats bent in half taking care of their precious fruits and greens. In spite of the attitude that growing vegetables is somehow archaic, community gardens are sprouting like weeds in our cities! Is this due to a renewed love of the land and the desire to eat fresher foods or a need to perpetuate traditions? Those are all good reasons, but it's more a very noble gesture that should incite us to maintain a bit of our collective memory. How? By reintroducing the idea of growing vegetables and fruits in our back yards, even if on a small scale. It begins by simply adding a few vegetables to our flowerbeds: a row of nicely rounded lettuce plants along the patio, a ground-cover of strawberries, a hedge of currants… and why not a pot of cherry tomatoes right next to the picnic table? What about herbs that can spread around between shrubs, cuddle up to perennials, and smell good all summer? Our background as a gardening people may be modest, but when we stop to take a look, we discover it is very much present nevertheless. It's up to us to discover it in order to perpetuate memories yet to come.

Moveable Gardens

You can grow anything in a pot: annuals, of course, but also perennials, ornamental grasses...

The joy of gardening in pots is that you can create, anywhere you want, dozens of little gardens from around the world. We don't always realize where all the annuals we grow in our summer gardens come from, but you can put together a little bit of Provence with lavender, a touch of Africa with zonal geraniums, and a piece of South America with begonias. What a trip for these plants that arrive as tiny babies in flats in spring and then, once in pots, explode with colour, amazing us with their blooms and their wide range of textures. Gardening in containers allows us to increase our palette of blooms while adding living colour to spots too narrow for flowerbeds. The problem is: which plants should you choose?

You can grow anything in a pot: annuals, of course, but also perennials, ornamental grasses and even vegetables like cherry tomatoes… and let's not forget herbs! All you have to do is to learn what light conditions they need, add a bit of rich planting soil, and place the plants according to their needs. A hot, sunny spot would be ideal for herbs like lavender and rosemary while hostas could be effectively used in shadier areas.

You can pot up one plant per container and create a unique composition of plants by mixing their textures to bring out contrasts. Big plants to the back and tall ones to the front! You can also create a mix of plants chosen for their colours and forms in a single large container.

There are a few rules to follow, though. For one, don't forget to include at least one-third foliage in the arrangement. That way the effect will be better balanced. Also, foliage allows flowering plants a bit of a break during their down times. You'll find magnificent foliage choices in ivies, plectranthus, ornamental grasses, and even many herbs. Another important rule to remember is that one and only one flowering plant must dominate in mixed containers: just one "thriller" per pot, or it's chaos! Complete the portrait by planting small-flowering annuals (fillers) all around the main plant and your pot is ready!

The extraordinary thing about containers is that you can move them and recompose your arrangements according to your whims and their flowerings. If you have a flowerbed, you can even insert pots among the permanent plants so as to bring out a particular colour or texture just at the peak of its development. Summer-flowering bulbs like dahlias and African lilies (*Agapanthus*) are best planted in pots and integrated into flowerbeds when their flowers appear. This method was very popular with the grande dame of the English garden, Gertrude Jekyll, who used to highlight the bloom of her favourite lilies by growing them in pots and inserting them in flowerbeds as they came into bloom. Growing tender bulbs in pots has the added advantage of making it easy to bring them indoors in the fall for their winter storage. Container gardens offer multiple possibilities. The more you use them, the better your gardens will look!

Exoticism is Within your Reach

It's a way of travelling without leaving home!

They say this summer is going to be hot and sunny, but you still need a change of scenery? No problem, as the tropics are no further away than your local garden centre! Banana plants, palm trees, oleanders, hibiscus, cannas and many more have been potted up and are ready for action! These plants from the Deep South share our patios, decks, and balconies where they adapt perfectly well. Not only that, but many of them can spend the winter in out homes and go back outside the following summer. Our fascination with

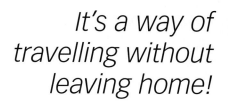

tropical plants goes back more than three hundred years when pot-grown orange and lemon trees were all the rage in royal courts and decorated Renaissance gardens. Enormous winter greenhouses, called orangeries, protected the tender fruits during the cold season while they spent the summer outdoors in full sun on vast terraces. This tradition with its long history is coming back into style. More and more magazines present landscaped patios full of tropical plants.

It's a way of travelling without leaving home… and travelling in style, at that! Sitting under a banana tree for a summer read or napping 'neath a blooming oleander, what could be better, right? Many, like hibiscus and bougainvilleas, offer us quantities of flowers whose colours brighten up the summer, but

elegant cachepot, these plants from far away never let you down and organize your space in an instant! The advantage of their large format is that they instantly create a sort of shelter, not only from the harsh rays of the sun, but from curious neighbours. A balcony in the tropics is the ultimate in stylishness!

others have graceful foliage that creates an exotic atmosphere on any deck. That's the case with, for example, ferns and certain palm trees that can adapt to light or even deep shade. Decked out in an

Gourmet Gardens

The ultimate reward for the gardener is to bite, with gusto, into the garden's first sun warmed tomato, dripping with finger-licking juice! After spring's hard labours, you can switch from a straw hat to a chef's hat… in order to prepare homemade dishes and special treats! From the simplist recipe to the most audacious culinary exploit, happiness comes from using perfectly ripe fruits and vegetables directly from the garden. What makes a better dessert than home-grown strawberries, currants, and blueberries? A hint of fresh herbs and your marinades and salad dressings will be a stunning success.

In the fall, after an orgy of delicious meals, it's time to start thinking of preparing your vegetable bed's soil for the upcoming season. After cultivating the soil deeply, apply Solmer Sea Compost over the entire surface to contribute to the soil nutrients necessary in producing future crops of great vegetables. When winter arrives, all that remains is to dream of the vegetable garden to come… and to consider how to extract a few more square feet of gardening space from the lawn so you can try a few new delicious beauties!

To learn more about the secrets of vegetable gardening, consult our section on edible plants: it's full of tastes and tricks that will make you a true gourmet gardener.

Feel the World Around You

These groups of forms and textures, peppered with colours, draw our attention...

Surrounded as we are by a multitude of sounds, by constant comings and goings, and by activities that just don't stop, it is perfectly normal to want to surround oneself with calm. Mother Nature responds well to this requirement by offering us her very best. She allows us to be able to appreciate all nature has to offer through our five senses: they come into action as soon as we approach her. At first it is through sight that nature captivates us and slows down our daily agitation. Natural landscapes, both large and small, always call to us: they are a constant source of inspiration for our creations. Observing nature, though, requires much more than sight and an attentive look allows us to take in all its beauties.

These groups of forms and textures, peppered with colours, draw our attention and slowly we step forward, curious… and who has never felt the desire to touch a plant! It's the second sense we encounter in the vegetable world. We creep up to leaves and softly feel their texture. Our fingers slide over their varnished surface and, if we see a flower, we like to run our fingers around it. It's a bit like shaking someone's hand! If the flower has a scent, the nose comes into action. They say that scent is the most powerful of the senses, that our memories register the slightest fragrance. Filling one's nostrils with the scent of roses, of lily of the valley, or of lavender is not something you quickly forget! Even though the fragrance of flowers is not originally designed for humans (Mother

Nature designed them to attract insect pollinators), the pleasure we obtain from perfumed plants certainly does make us want to grow them! And that's where the wind comes into play, moving through the branches and making the leaves dance.

These delicate sounds enchant us and, if the wind grows stronger, the leaves reply to its force, the weather changes… Nature offers other sounds, like the sound of water. Be it in the form of raindrops or smooth curtains from a cascade, water beautifully accompanies the other songs of the garden. Finally, when we love plants, we often have but one other desire: to taste them! If certain vegetables make those who eat them happy, and if lots of others are ingested as medications, for many other ornamental plants, only the flowers are edible. Eating flowers is a memorable experience. It's a true pleasure that tickles the taste buds. The best way of getting the taste of a garden is to chow down on a variety of plants that please the eye and the spirit. The garden should overflow with pleasant odours, soft murmurings, shimmering colours, and unforgettable flavours! That's the way to a garden full of good… sense!

Perennials

Platycodon sp.

As soon as spring arrives, perennials start to grow. Called perennials because their root system allows them to store up reserves for the following year, perennials come back faithfully again and again. Their multitude of forms, foliage textures, brilliant flower colours, heights and perfumes makes this group of plants one of the most popular. The choice of perennials you'll find at your Passion Jardins garden centre is so vast you'll be able to complete your compositions with panache. Perennials like company and always look most spectacular when in mass plantings. They'll also look better when placed in front of shrubs to cover their absence during early spring, since perennials must start from zero at the beginning of each new year. Since dividing perennials is so simple, your flowerbeds will grow quickly and fill in beautifully.

Lewisia sp.

Achillea millefolium 'Paprika'
'Paprika' Common Yarrow

[|] 50 cm [↔] 40 cm [❋] 6-9 [☀] [ZONE 3] [🦋] [🦌]

A very hardy drought-resistant cultivar bearing uniquely coloured flowers. Prefers moderately rich, cool, moist soil, but also prospers in poorer soil.

Achillea 'Terracotta'
'Terracotta' Hybrid Yarrow

(PV)

[|] 75 cm [↔] 50 cm [❋] 6-9 [☀] [⊘] [ZONE 3] [🦋] [🦌]

Flowers with changing colours that blend with finely cut foliage. Very reliable and always in bloom, it grows in moderately rich, cool, well-drained soil, but supports drought well.

Aconitum cammarum 'Bicolor'
Bicolour Monkshood

[|] 100 cm [↔] 50 cm [❋] 7-8 [☀] [⊘] [ZONE 3] [🦌]

Looking for extended bloom at the end of the summer? This tall perennial is pest resistant and grows well in rich, slightly moist, acid soil.

Ajuga reptans 'Burgundy Glow'
'Burgundy Glow' Bugle Weed

(PV)

[|] 15 cm [↔] 20 cm [❋] 5-6 [☀] [⊘] [🌤] [ZONE 3] [🦌]

Pretty multicoloured foliage, ideal for accompanying perennials in the shade garden. Does best in rich, cool, well-drained soil, but tolerates acid soil.

Ajuga reptans 'Catlin's Giant'
'Catlin's Giant' Bugle Weed

						ZONE 3	
30 cm	30 cm	5-6					

Groundcover producing very large leaves in shades of purple and dark green. Good subject for growing under conifers in acid soil, but it prefers rich, cool, well-drained soil.

Ajuga reptans 'Chocolate Chip'
'Chocolate Chip' Bugle Weed

						ZONE 3	
10 cm	25 cm	5-6					

The ideal groundcover for dense shade, in rich, cool, well-drained soil. Also tolerates acid soil. Small, narrow, bronze-coloured leaves. Irresistible!

Alcea rosea
Hollyhock

				ZONE 2	
100-165 cm	45-60 cm	7-8			

Tall flower stalks bearing cup-shaped blooms. Very drought resistant, perfect for decorating the back of the border in rich, cool, well-drained soil. Sometimes self sows. Biennial.

Alchemilla mollis
Lady's Mantle

				ZONE 3	
40-60 cm	60 cm	6-8			

The perfect plant, adapted to all growing conditions. Always pretty and pest-free, it forms beautiful borders along flower beds. Prefers rich, moist soil, but grows in light, heavy, acid, or poor soil.

Anemone hybrida 'Honorine Jobert'
'Honorine Jobert' Hybrid Anemone

(PV)

🔼 90 cm ↔ 45 cm ❀ 9-10 ☀ 🌤 ⓩ4

Very popular! Pure white fall flowers on a vigorous and always healthy plant. Adores rich, slightly acid soils.

Anemone hupehensis 'September Charm'
'September Charm' Japanese Anemone

🔼 70 cm ↔ 45 cm ❀ 9-10 ☀ 🌤 ⓩ4

Vigorous cultivar with satin pink flowers. Essential for the fall garden in rich, cool, well-drained soil. Will grow in slightly acid soil.

Anthemis tinctoria 'Wargrave'
'Wargrave' Golden Marguerite

🔼 90 cm ↔ 60 cm ❀ 7-9 ☀ ⓩ5 🪴

Superb clear yellow blooms that last all summer, accompanied by beautiful, finely cut foliage. Creates great masses of flowers even in poor soil.

Aquilegia flabellata 'Cameo' series
'Cameo' Dwarf Columbine

🔼 15 cm ↔ 20 cm ❀ 5-6 ☀ 🌤 ⓩ4 🪴

Dwarf cultivar with large, early-blooming flowers. Perfect for rock gardens and retaining walls, in rich, slightly acid, cool, well-drained soil.

Aquilegia vulgaris 'Nora Barlow'
'Nora Barlow' Common Columbine

⬍ 75 cm ⬌ 40 cm ✻ 6-7 ☀ ☼ ZONE 3

Unique and spectacular double flowers. Tall columbine that requires little garden space. Perect as a filler in rich, cool, well-drained soil.

Arabis caucasica 'Snowcap'
'Snowcap' Rock-Cress

⬍ 15 cm ⬌ 35 cm ✻ 4-5 ☀ ZONE 3

Small creeping plant flowering very early. Perfectly adapted to rock gardens and edging in very well-drained soil, either rich or poor. Drought tolerant.

Arenaria montana
Mountain Sandwort

⬍ 15 cm ⬌ 30 cm ✻ 5-6 ☀ ☼ ZONE 3

Remarkable! A low-growing cushion of tiny white flowers in early spring. This perennial for well-drained soils does perfectly in poor, stony, dry soil. Ideal for difficult spots.

Arenaria verna 'Aurea'
Golden Sandwort

⬍ 5 cm ⬌ 30 cm ✻ 6-7 ☀ ☼ ZONE 3

Good groundcover for planting between pavers and flagstones. This tiny, low-growing carpeting plant grows well in poor, stony, dry soil.

Armeria maritima 'Rubrifolia'
Red-leaved Sea Thrift

15 cm 15 cm 5-7

Superb fine bronze-tinted foliage makes this perennial unique. Always appreciated in rock gardens or as a border plant. Needs moderately rich soil, a bit on the dry side and very well drained.

Artemisia stelleriana 'Silver Brocade'
'Silver Brocade' Beach Wormund

15 cm 30 cm

Attractive deeply cut, silky grey foliage. Perfect for creating contrasts in mixed borders. Grows well in poor, dry soil, but prefers slightly alkaline conditions.

Artemisia schmidtiana 'Silver Mound'
Silver Mound Artemisia

30 cm 40 cm

Very easy to grow. Beautiful silky, aromatic, light grey foliage. Even grows in poor, dry soil. Very drought tolerant. A classic!

Aruncus aethusifolius
Dwarf Goatsbeard

25 cm 30 cm 6-7

Like a tiny astilbe, this plant needs little care. It grows readily in rich, acid, slightly moist soil. Charming!

Aruncus dioicus
Goatsbeard

100-150 cm   90 cm   6-7

Superb giant-size perennial with light airy blooms. Plant in masses at the back of the bed, in rich, acid, slightly moist soil. Easy to grow.

Asclepias tuberosa
Butterfly Weed

75 cm   40 cm   7-8

Essential for attracting monarch butterflies! Once established, butterfly weed tolerates very dry soil. Prefers moderately rich, acid soil.

Asperula odorata
Sweet Woodruff

20 cm   40 cm   5-6

The ideal groundcover under shrubs and small trees. Grows vigorously in rich, somewhat alkaline, cool, well-drained soil.

Aster alpinus 'Happy End'
'Happy End' Alpine Aster

30 cm   35 cm   5-6

Forms a low-growing mass of dark pink flowers at the beginning of summer. A must-have for rock gardens and alpine gardens in moderately rich, cool, well-drained soil.

Aster dumosus 'Sapphire'
'Sapphire' Aster

⊡ ⟷ ❀ ☀ [ZONE 4] 🐾 🦋 🦌

40 cm · 40 cm · 8-10

Low-growing, disease-resistant and long-blooming…
what more could you ask of an aster? Likes rich, cool,
well-drained soil.

Astilbe arendsii 'Diamant'
'Diamant' Astilbe

(PV)

⊡ ⟷ ❀ ☀ ☼ ❄ [ZONE 3] 🦋 🦌

80 cm · 50 cm · 7-8

Beautiful dense, compact astilbe that is just as attractive
alone as in mass plantings. Needs slightly moist soil and
prefers rich, slightly acid soil.

Astilbe arendsii 'Fanal'
'Fanal' Astilbe

⊡ ⟷ ❀ ☀ ☼ ❄ [ZONE 3] 🦋 🦌

45 cm · 50 cm · 7-8

Popular low-care cultivar, very easy to grow. Bright
flowers against dark green bronze-tinted foliage.
Grows in rich, somewhat acid, slightly moist soil.

Astilbe chinensis 'Pumila'
Dwarf Chinese Astilbe

⊡ ⟷ ❀ ☀ ☼ ❄ [ZONE 3] 🦋 🦌

25 cm · 20 cm · 8-9

Charming narrow spikes on somewhat drought-resistant
plants. Best planted in rich, cool, well-drained soil. Always
popular.

Astilbe chinensis 'Vision in Red'
'Vision in Red' Chinese Astilbe

(PV)

| 45 cm | 45 cm | 8 | | | ZONE 4 | | |

Resistant. Flowers in dense stalks, always easy to grow. Beautiful in mass plantings and mixed with other perennials in rich, cool, well-drained soil. Tolerates a bit of drought.

Astilbe thunbergii 'Ostrich Plume'
Ostrich Plume Astilbe

| 90 cm | 50 cm | 8 | | | ZONE 4 | | |

Spectacular feathery, arching blooms. Always popular with gardeners. Easy to grow in rich, slightly moist soil.

Astilbe simplicifolia 'Sprite'
'Sprite' Dwarf Astible

| 30 cm | 25 cm | 7 | | | ZONE 4 | | |

Delicate flowers that are very effective in flower beds and near water gardens. Very easy to grow, this astilbe needs slightly moist soil, ideally rich and somewhat acid.

Astilboides tabularis
Shieldleaf

| 100-120 cm | 75-100 cm | 6-7 | | | ZONE 4 |

Stunning plant with huge round leaves that can measure up to 60 cm in diameter. It forms beautiful masses in moist, rich soil. Attractive in shade near stream beds.

Astrantia major 'Lars'
'Lars' Masterwort

⬍ ⬌ ❀ ☀ ❄ ◌ ZONE 4

70 cm 40 cm 7-10

Remarkable! Masterwort is very easy to grow, pest resistant and its blooms last several months. Even though it prefers moderately rich, somewhat alkaline, cool, well-drained soil, it adapts to most conditions.

Brunnera macrophylla 'Jack Frost'
'Jack Frost' Brunnera

⬍ ⬌ ❀ ❄ ◌ ZONE 3

30 cm 45 cm 5-6

Remarkable silver leaves with green veining. Produces tiny clear blue flowers in spring. Indispensable in the shade garden, in rich, slightly moist soil.

Bellis perennis 'Pomponette' series
Pomponette English Daisy

⬍ ⬌ ❀ ☀ ❄ ZONE 3

10 cm 20 cm 5-6

Adorable little plant with double to semi-double flowers. Grow it as an edging plant for borders or in small groups of three to five plants in rich, cool, well-drained soil. Biennial.

Campanula carpatica 'Blue Clips'
'Blue Clips' Carpathian Bellflower

(PV)

⬍ ⬌ ❀ ☀ ❄ ZONE 3 🐝 🦋

20 cm 30 cm 6-9

Unbeatable perennial that is very easy to grow and blooms non-stop from spring through fall. Will grow in all soil types, poor or rich, cool or dry, alkaline or acid, but always well-drained.

Campanula carpatica 'White Clips'
'White Clips' Carpathian Bellflower

⬍ 20 cm ⬌ 30 cm ❋ ☀ ❄ ⬡ ZONE 3 🌱 🦌

20 cm   30 cm   6-9

Perfect for novice gardeners. Always in bloom and pest-free, this tough perennial will grow in all types of soil… as long as they are well-drained.

Campanula garganica 'Dickson's Gold'
'Dickson's Gold' Gargano Bellflower

⬍ 15 cm ⬌ 30 cm ❋ ❄ ZONE 4

15 cm   30 cm   6-8

A good choice along meandering paths. Very luminous yellow foliage. Grows in moderately rich, cool, well-drained, slightly alkaline soil.

Campanula persicifolia
Peachleaf Bellflower

Our favorite picks

⬍ 65-100 cm ⬌ 30-45 cm ❋ ☀ ❄ ZONE 3

65-100 cm   30-45 cm   6-7

Attractive plant with bell-shaped flowers. Easy to insert among other perennials in the mixed border to create romantic combinations. Prefers moderately rich, cool, moist soil. Popular.

Campanula portenschlagiana (syn.: C. muralis)
Dalmatian Bellflower

⬍ 10 cm ⬌ 30 cm ❋ ☀ ❄ ZONE 3 🌱 🦌

10 cm   30 cm   5-9

Always just as popular massed along flower borders or near retaining walls. Prefers slightly alkaline soil, but grows well in moderately rich, cool, well-drained soil.

Campanula poscharskyana 'Blue Gown'
'Blue Gown' Serbian Bellflower

⬍ 20 cm ⬌ 15 cm ZONE 6-9

Dwarf variety with large blooms that can just as easily be grown in containers as in borders. Tolerates light soil, but grows best in moderately rich, somewhat alkaline, cool, well-drained soil.

Campanula punctata 'Bowl of Cherries'
'Bowl of Cherries' Spotted Bellflower

⬍ 40 cm ⬌ 40 cm ZONE 6-8

Large flowers like upside-down cups on compact plants. Very floriferous. Plant in groups in rich, slightly acid, cool, well-drained soil.

Centaurea montana 'Gold Bullion'
'Gold Bullion' Perennial Cornflower

Our favorite picks

⬍ 30 cm ⬌ 40 cm ZONE 5-6

Fascinating perennial with yellow foliage for great contrasts in the flower bed. Prefers moderately rich, cool, moist soil, but tolerates dry, poor conditions.

Cerastium tomentosum
Snow-in-Summer

⬍ 15 cm ⬌ 45 cm ZONE 5-6

Here's a groundcover recommended for rock gardens and flower beds with soil that is rather light, poor, and dry. Popular species with silver leaves. Attractive at the base of roses.

Ceratostigma plumbaginoides
Leadwort

20-30 cm 40-60 cm 7-9

Interesting groundcover for fall colour with red and bronze foliage and dark blue flowers. Very adaptable, it grows just as well in sun or partial shade and in just about any soil.

Chrysanthemum 'Clara Curtis'
'Clara Curtis' Fall Mum

70 cm 40 cm 8-10

Unbeatable for spectacular fall blooms! Easy to grow, tough plant, which is why it is so popular with gardeners. Moderately rich, cool, well-drained soil.

Chelone obliqua
Rose Turtlehead

60-90 cm 45-60 cm 8-10

Superb mass of dark pink flowers in late summer and fall. Robust, vigorous plant if grown in moist soil. It prefers moderately rich, acid soil.

Cimicifuga ramosa 'Brunette'
(syn.: Actaea simplex 'Brunette')
'Brunette' Bugbane

Our favorite picks

90-120 cm 60-90 cm 8-10

Even in dense shade, the dark purple foliage and the pinkish blooms of 'Brunette' grow with great vigour. Adores rich, slightly acid, cool, well-drained soil.

Cimicifuga ramosa 'Atropurpurea'
(syn.: *Actaea simplex* 'Atropurpurea')
Purpleleaf Bugbane

175 cm 60 cm 8-10

Attractive plant, both for its purple foliage and its tall, narrow flower spikes late in the season. Does well even in dense shade and prefers rich, slightly acid, cool, well-drained soil.

Convallaria majalis
Lily-of-the-Valley

20 cm 30 cm 5

How can you resist the sweet scent of this vigorous groundcover? It fills in empty spaces in no time, especially if the soil is rich, a bit acid and moist. Grows well in many soil types.

Coreopsis grandiflora 'Rising Sun'
'Rising Sun' Coreopsis

Our favorite picks

60 cm 45 cm 6-8

A champion that reaches full bloom the first year you plant it. A vigorous, long-blooming cultivar. Plant in rich, somewhat acid, cool, well-drained soil. Tolerates drought and heat.

Coreopsis auricularia 'Zamfir'
'Zamfir' Dwarf Coreopsis

45 cm 45 cm 6-8

Surprising tubular florets on a tough perennial. Long-blooming so you have time to appreciate it. Likes moderately rich, somewhat acid, cool, well-drained soil.

Coreopsis verticillata 'Moonbeam'
'Moonbeam' Threadleaf Coreopsis

Our favorite picks

🔼 ↔ ❄ ☀ ⓩ🅝ⓔ③ 🐦 🦋 🦌
40 cm   40 cm   6-10

Still very popular! Bushy plant with fine foliage, entirely covered with small lemon yellow flowers. Plant in moderately rich, somewhat acid, cool, well-drained soil. Drought tolerant.

Coreopsis verticillata 'Zagreb'
'Zagreb' Threadleaf Coreopsis

🔼 ↔ ❄ ☀ ⓩ🅝ⓔ③ 🐦 🦋 🦌
40 cm   40 cm   7-10

Prolific and floriferous plant with large bright yellow flowers. Superb planted in masses with other perennials in moderately rich, cool, moist soil. Drought tolerant.

Delphinium grandiflorum 'Blue Butterfly'
'Blue Butterfly' Large-flowered Delphinium

Our favorite picks

🔼 ↔ ❄ ☀ ⓩ🅝ⓔ③ 🐦 🦋 🦌
25-40 cm   30 cm   6-9

The best companion plant for plants with spectacular flowers like lilies, dahlias and roses. Constantly in bloom, it grows in moderately rich, cool, well-drained soil.

Delphinium grandiflorum 'Summer' *series*
'Summer' Delphinium

New

🔼 ↔ ❄ ☀ ⓩ🅝ⓔ④ 🦌
30-45 cm   30 cm   6-9

You'll fall in love with this compact and very floriferous series. Flowers the first year. For a great show, plant in rich, cool, well-drained soil in groups of three to five plants. Drought tolerant and easy to grow.

Delphinium elatum 'Magic Fountains' series
'Magic Fountains' Delphinium

⬍ 80-100 cm ↔ 40-60 cm ❋ 6-7 ☀ ZONE 3 ⓜ

One of the most beautiful blooms in the perennial border. This compact variety has strong flower stems. Needs rich, cool, well-drained soil. Plant in small groups.

Dianthus deltoides 'Brilliant'
'Brilliant' Maiden Pink

⬍ 15 cm ↔ 45 cm ❋ 6-10 ☀ ☀ ZONE 3 ⓜ

Generous bloom that entirely hides the foliage. Makes a good edging plant and a small groundcover for rock gardens and flower beds. Likes light, cool, well-drained soil.

Dianthus gratianopolitanus 'Firewitch'
'Firewitch' Cheddar Pink

⬍ 15 cm ↔ 15 cm ❋ 5-7 ☀ ☀ ZONE 3 ⓜ

Small plant bearing superb magenta flowers above grey-blue foliage. Does best in the light, dry soil of rock gardens and flower beds.

Dianthus gratianopolitanus 'Frosty Fire'
'Frosty Fire' Cheddar Pink

⬍ 25 cm ↔ 30 cm ❋ 6-9 ☀ ☀ ZONE 3 ⓜ

Vibrant semi-double flowers above grey-blue leaves. The ideal subject for a rock garden or at the base of a wall in poor, dry, slightly alkaline soil.

Dicentra 'King of Hearts'
'King of Hearts' Hybrid Bleeding Heart

20-30 cm 35 cm 5-10

Always in bloom, it grows in full sun or dense shade. Beautiful bluish heat-tolerant foliage. Likes moderately rich, cool, moist soil.

Dicentra 'Luxuriant'
'Luxuriant' Pacific Bleeding Heart

30 cm 30 cm 5-10

A beautiful perennial with a proven track record. Tolerates a wide range of growing conditions. Very floriferous with beautiful bluish foliage. Prefers moderately rich, cool, moist soil.

Dicentra spectabilis 'Gold Heart'
'Gold Heart' Bleeding Heart

70 cm 60 cm 5-6

A classic revisited, this time with very luminous gold foliage on orange-pink stems. This bleeding heart requires a cool spot in moderately rich, well-drained soil. Unusual!

Digitalis purpurea 'Foxy'
'Foxy' Purple Foxglove

75 cm 30 cm 6-7

Always appreciated for its unbeatable blooms. Beautiful grown with roses and perennial geraniums. Loves rich, somewhat acid, well-drained soil. Biennial.

Echinacea 'Big Sky Sundown'
'Sundown' Echinacea

New

60-90 cm 45-60 cm 7-9

In shades of orange, this echinacea with slightly drooping petals does best in cool, well-drained, rather rich soil. You can't miss it in the garden, whether it is grown on its own or in clusters. Tolerates drought once established.

Echinacea 'Big Sky Sunrise'
'Sunrise' Echinacea

Our favorite picks

75-90 cm 45-60 cm 7-9

Never before seen in an echinacea! Highly perfumed flowers in pure clear yellow. A vigorous, well-branched plant, floriferous and easy to grow in cool, well-drained, rich soil.

Echinacea 'Big Sky Sunset'
'Sunset' Echinacea

Our favorite picks

60-90 cm 45 cm 7-9

Unique colour! An essential addition to the butterfly garden along with agastache and butterfly bush. Easy to grow, requiring no maintenance, it grows best in cool, well-drained, rather rich soil.

Echinacea 'Harvest Moon'
'Harvest Moon' Echinacea

75-90 cm 45-60 cm 7-9

Easy to grow, 'Harvest Moon' is a vigorous echinacea with delightfully perfumed tangerine yellow flowers. Reblooms generously. Plant in cool, well-drained, rather rich soil.

Echinacea 'Orange Meadowbrite'
(syn.: *Echinacea* 'Art's Pride')
'Orange Meadowbrite' Echinacea

PV

🔼 ↔️ ❋ ☀️ ❄️ 🆉🅾🅽🅴3 🐦 Ⓜ️ 🌱 🦌

60-90 cm 40-60 cm 7-9

The latest trend in echinaceas! The flowers in shades of pink to dark orange create a palette like a beautiful sunset, plus they have a spicy scent. Rich, cool, well-drained soil.

Echinacea purpurea 'Ruby Star'
(syn.: *Echinacea purpurea* 'Rubinstern')
'Ruby Star' Echinacea

Our favorite picks

🔼 ↔️ ❋ ☀️ ❄️ 🆉🅾🅽🅴4 🐦 Ⓜ️ 🌱

100 cm 45 cm 7-9

A large-flowered selection in pure pink with upright petals. A robust, rock-solid plant that prefers rich, cool, well-drained soil.

Echinops bannaticus 'Blue Glow'
'Blue Glow' Globe Thistle

🔼 ↔️ ❋ ☀️ ❄️ 🆉🅾🅽🅴3 Ⓜ️ 🦌

100-125 cm 75-90 cm 7-8

A unique tall perennial with spiny foliage, a greyish tinge and perfectly round flowers. It grows just as well in rich or poor soil, whether moist or dry. Easy to grow.

Eryngium amethystinum
Sea Holly

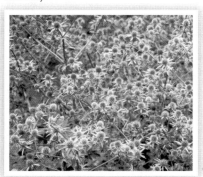

🔼 ↔️ ❋ ☀️ 🆉🅾🅽🅴2 🐦 Ⓜ️ 🦌

60 cm 30 cm 7-8

Architectural plant with blue-grey spiny foliage. A champion in light and dry soil. Also likes moderately rich and slightly alkaline soil.

Eupatorium rugosum 'Chocolate'
Chocolate Snakeroot

⬍ ⬌ ❄ ☀ ❆ ⁿ³ 🦋 🌱
120 cm 90 cm 8-9

A mass of green leaves tinted dark purple over which hover masses of white flowers that butterflies adore. Grows well in heavy soil in a rich, cool, well-drained substrate.

Euphorbia myrsinites
Myrtle Spurge

Our *favorite* picks

⬍ ⬌ ❄ ☀ ⁿ⁴ 🌱
20 cm 30 cm 5-6

Fabulous little perennial, perfect as an edging plant and in rock gardens. Does best in poor, rocky, alkaline, dry soil. Beautiful bluish foliage contrasting with lemon yellow flowers.

Filipendula purpurea 'Elegans'
Japanese Meadosweet

⬍ ⬌ ❄ ☀ ❆ ⁿ³ 🦋 ▦
110 cm 35 cm 7

A long-lived perennial with frothy, original flowers. A beautiful addtion to the mixed border in rich, slightly moist soil.

Filipendula rubra 'Venusta'
Queen of the Prairie

PV

⬍ ⬌ ❄ ☀ ❆ ⁿ³ 🦋 ▦
180 cm 50 cm 6-8

Very tall perennial, perfect for the background of a flower bed, in rich, slightly moist soil. Tough and durable, the flowers are simply magnificent!

Gaillardia x *grandiflora* 'Burgundy'
(syn.: *Gaillardia* x *grandiflora* 'Burgunder')
'Burgundy' Blanketflower

🔼 60 cm ↔ 30 cm ❄ 7-10 ☀ ☀ [ZONE 3] 🦋 ✂

Unusual colour for a blanketflower. Always in bloom, yet requiring little effort: just plant it in the border in moderately rich, cool, moist soil. Comes up late in spring.

Gaillardia 'Arizona Sun'
'Arizona Sun' Blanketflower

🔼 20-25 cm ↔ 25-30 cm 7-10 ☀ ☀ [ZONE 4] 🦋 📋

Dazzling perennial with extended bloom that tolerates transient periods of drought. This large-flowered perennial grows in rich, cool, well-drained soil. Even the dried flower is attractive.

Gaillardia 'Fanfare'
'Fanfare' Blanketflower

Our favorite picks

🔼 45 cm ↔ 45 cm 6-10 ☀ [ZONE 3] 🦋 ✂

Surprising florets shaped like trumpets decorate this very floriferous and compact perennial. In containers or in the garden, it is happiest in moderately rich, cool, well-drained soil. Tolerates short periods of drought.

Gaura lindheimeri 'Corrie's Gold'
'Corrie's Gold' Gaura

🔼 75-90 cm ↔ 60 cm 6-10 ☀ ☀ [ZONE 5] 🦋

The gold-variegated leaves give an original appearance to this gracefully blooming perennial. Does just as well in poor soil as rich. Tolerates drought, but prefers somewhat acid, cool, well-drained soil.

Geranium cinereum 'Ballerina'
'Ballerina' Greyleaf Geranium

20 cm   30 cm   6-9

Always a favourite for the rock garden with its greyish foliage and continuous bloom. Recommended for poor, stony, dry soil. Grows just as well in acid as alkaline soil.

Geranium 'Rozanne'
'Rozanne' Geranium

50 cm   60 cm   6-10

New! Very floriferous and vigorous variety with pure purple flowers and a white eye. Pest-free, it prospers in rich, cool, well-drained soil, either acid or alkaline.

Geranium sanguineum 'Max Frei'
'Max Frei' Bloody Geranium

20 cm   30 cm   6-9

Brightly coloured, it is ideal in association with other flowering perennials or for use as a groundcover. Maintenance-free, this geranium grows in rich, somewhat alkaline, cool, well-drained soil.

Gypsophila paniculata 'Pink Fairy'
'Pink Fairy' Baby's Breath

90 cm   60 cm   6-9

Pink version of baby's breath. This superb filler plant tolerates drought but prefers a moderately rich environment in slightly alkaline, cool, well-drained soil.

Gypsophila repens 'Rosea'
Pink-flowered Creeping Baby's Breath

15 cm 60 cm 6-7

Small carpeting plant that does well in poor, rocky, slightly alkaline, dry soil. Use as an edging plant for borders, in rock gardens or near retaining walls.

Helenium 'Moerheim Beauty'
'Moerheim Beauty' Sneezeweed

PV

80-90 cm 60 cm 7-9

Generous fall bloom in shades of yellow and orange. Superb in association with grasses and other late-blooming perennials. For rich, cool, well-drained soil.

Helenium 'Ruby Tuesday'
'Ruby Tuesday' Sneezeweed

New

50 cm 30cm 7-9

A sneezeweed with extended bloom. Very compact variety. Ideal for rich, cool, well-drained soil. Remove faded flowers to extend the bloom.

Helenium 'Rubinzwerg' *(syn.: H. 'Ruby Dwarf')*
'Rubinzwerg' Sneezeweed

New

75 cm 45-60 cm 7-8

Red velvet petals extend around a dark brown and yellow centre. This bright colour contrasts beautifully with the green foliage. Compact perennial prefering rich, cool, well-drained soil. Beautiful cut flower.

Helenium 'Mardi Gras'
'Mardi Gras' Sneezeflower

90-120 cm   60-90 cm   7-9

A shower of multicolour flowers in hot shades that last over six consecutive weeks. Beautiful grouped together at the back of a border in rich, cool, well-drained soil. Excellent cut flower. Tolerates dry soil.

Heliopsis helianthoides 'Summer Night'
'Summer Night' Oxeye

Our favorite picks

90-120 cm   60 cm   7-9

Vigorous and stately, this cultivar stands out from the crowd due to its double flowers and its lightly tinted bronze foliage. Beautiful and striking, it does best in rich, slightly acid, cool, well-drained soil.

Helianthus decapetalus 'Loddon Gold'
'Loddon Gold' Thinleaf Sunflower

120-150 cm   45-60 cm   8-10

Easy to grow even in the worst conditions, including poor, dry and even heavy soil. Very pretty double yellow flowers. Prefers rich, slightly moist soil.

Heliopsis helianthoides 'Loraine Sunshine'
'Loraine Sunshine' Oxeye

75 cm   45 cm   6-8

An attention-getter! A beautiful marriage of green veins and creamy white foliage with very long-lasting golden yellow blooms. Prefers a rich and somewhat acid soil, and tolerates dry soil.

Helleborus niger 'Ivory Prince'
'Ivory Prince' Lenten Rose

   ZONE 5
40-60 cm   40 cm   4-5

A generous quantity of white flowers with a pinkish tinge that rise well above the foliage. Grows best in rich, rather heavy, somewhat alkaline, moist soil.

Hemerocallis 'Always Afternoon'
'Always Afternoon' Daylily

     ZONE 3
50 cm   45-60 cm   7-8

Big pink flowers with a plum-coloured stripe and a green heart. Long-blooming, very reliable plant that is pest resistant. Grows in many types of soil. Drought tolerant.

Hemerocallis 'Bela Lugosi'
'Bela Lugosi' Daylily

  ZONE 3
75 cm   60 cm   7-8

Very intense flower on a vigorous, very hardy daylily. Like all daylilies, it is very easy to grow. Prefers rich, somewhat acid, cool, well-drained soil. One of the darkest daylilies.

Hemerocallis 'Forty Second Street'
'Forty Second Street' Daylily

     ZONE 4
60 cm   60 cm   7

Interesting double light pink flower with a darker centre on a very easy to grow plant. Grows well in rich, somewhat acid, cool, well-drained soil. Generous blooms.

Hemerocallis 'Happy Returns'
'Happy Returns' Daylily

35-40 cm   45-60 cm   6-8

Impressive quantity of small lemon yellow flowers on a miniature plant. Never stops blooming! Grows very well in many soil conditions. Drought tolerant.

Hemerocallis 'Pardon Me'
'Pardon Me' Daylily

45 cm   60-75 cm   7-8

Miniature variety with tiny, striking flowers, delightfully scented and long-lasting. Ideal for borders and decorative containers. Edible flowers. Rich, cool, well-drained soil.

Hemerocallis 'Purple de Oro'
'Purple de Oro' Daylily

30 cm   45 cm   6-9

A mauve to carmine pink version, according to soil type, of the famous 'Stella de Oro' daylily. Very floriferous, blooming from early summer to fall, and easy to grow. A winning selection that is more and more popular! Rich, cool, well-drained soil.

Hemerocallis 'Stella de Oro'
'Stella de Oro' Daylily

30 cm   45 cm   6-9

Indispensable! A great favourite for its small flowers that bloom throughout the growing season. Tough and maintenance-free. The perfect plant! Tolerates all soils, but prefers rich, somewhat acid, cool, well-drained soil.

Hemerocallis 'Strawberry Candy'
'Strawberry Candy' Daylily

65 cm 60 cm 6-7

Multi-prize winner. Big beautiful flowers with a fringed margin. Very vigorous plant with extended bloom. Grows in rich, cool, slightly acid, well-drained soil. Drought tolerant.

Heuchera 'Amber Waves'
'Amber Waves' Heuchera

30 cm 30-40 cm 6-7

Superb wavy foliage in amber and gold. One single plant is all it takes to brighten up the flower bed! For rich, cool, well-drained soil, but tolerates poor, dry soil.

Heuchera 'Chocolate Ruffles'
'Chocolate Ruffles' Heuchera

60 cm 45 cm 7

Large variety with dark foliage for use as a groundcover. Drought resistant. Easy to grow, this heuchera grows in many types of soil.

Heuchera 'Dolce Peach Melba'
'Dolce Peach Melba' Heuchera

20-40 cm 30 cm 7

Highly appreciated in the shade garden, this cultivar with variable foliage colours is ideal for both containers and flower beds. Prefers rich, cool, well-drained soil.

Heuchera 'Lime Rickey'
'Lime Rickey' Heuchera

(PV)

40 cm 40 cm 6-7

Astounding! Very luminous chartreuse foliage, perfect for creating contrasts, whether in containers or in flower beds. Grows in cool, well-drained soil, either rich or poor.

Heuchera 'Cherries Jubilee'
'Cherries Jubilee' Heuchera

15-30 cm 30-40 cm 8-10

Heuchera with foliage spotted purple and grey. Ideal for landscape design: let your imagination run wild and dare to create original compositions. Prefers rich, cool, well-drained soil.

Heuchera 'Mercury'
'Mercury' Heuchera

New

25-35 cm 30 cm 7-8

Mint green foliage marbled dark purple. Grow in group plantings at the base of perennials and shrubs with green leaves. Interesting too in mixed arrangements. Prefers rich, cool, well-drained soil.

Heucherella 'Sunspot'
'Sunspot' Heucherella

Our favorite picks

45 cm 45 cm 6-8

Superb golden yellow leaf with a brown spot in the centre. The bloom is just as spectacular. Needs somewhat acid conditions and prefers rich, cool, well-drained soil.

Heucherella 'Kimono'
'Kimono' Heucherella

⟨🔲⟩ ⟨↔⟩ ⟨❄⟩ ⟨☀⟩ ⟨☀⟩ ⟨♻⟩ ⟨ZONE 3⟩ ⟨🌱⟩ ⟨🦋⟩
45 cm 45 cm 6-8

Beautiful green leaf with dark veins, its color and shade change throughout the season. An essential addition to the shade garden in cool, rich, well-drained soil.

Hibiscus moscheutos 'Southern Belle' series
'Southern Belle' Hibiscus

Our favorite picks

⟨🔲⟩ ⟨↔⟩ ⟨❄⟩ ⟨☀⟩ ⟨ZONE 5⟩ ⟨🌱⟩ ⟨🦋⟩ ⟨🚫⟩
120 cm 80 cm 8-9

Apparently too beautiful to be real, yet these huge flowers bloom continuously until frost. Slow to come up in spring. Appreciates rich, slightly acid and rather moist soil.

Hosta 'Big Daddy'
'Big Daddy' Hosta

Our favorite picks

⟨🔲⟩ ⟨↔⟩ ⟨❄⟩ ⟨☀⟩ ⟨♻⟩ ⟨ZONE 3⟩ ⟨🌱⟩
60 cm 90 cm 7

Big hosta with thick, embossed and bluish leaves. Does best in dense shade and cool, well-drained soil.

Hosta 'Fire and Ice'
'Fire and Ice' Hosta

(PV)

⟨🔲⟩ ⟨↔⟩ ⟨❄⟩ ⟨☀⟩ ⟨ZONE 3⟩ ⟨🌱⟩
45 cm 25 cm 8

Interesting both for its intense mauve flowers and its twisted, dark green foliage with a creamy white centre. Powerful! Grows in rich, cool, well-drained soil. Slug resistant.

Hosta 'Francee'
'Francee' Hosta

45-60 cm   90-115 cm   8

The perfect groundcover hosta. Decorative foliage that maintains its variegation in the sun. Well-loved by novice gardeners, it can be planted in rich, cool, well-drained soil. Slug resistant.

Hosta sieboldiana 'Frances Williams'
'Frances Williams' Hosta

80 cm   100 cm   7

Huge easy-to-grow hosta that is very popular! Thick, slug-resistant leaves. For flower bed borders in rich, somewhat acid, slightly moist soil.

Hosta 'Patriot'
'Patriot' Hosta

45 cm   75 cm   7

A hosta with personality! Maintains its contrasting colours all summer. Plant in rich, cool, well-drained soil. Slug resistant.

Hosta sieboldii 'Sum and Substance'
'Sum and Substance' Hosta

(PV)

80 cm   150 cm   8

One of the largest hostas on the market! Marvellous chartreuse green foliage, with sunken veins. Appreciates cool soil. Slug resistant. Immense!

Hosta 'Sun Power'
'Sun Power' Hosta

⬍ ⬌ ❀ ☀ ❀ ☁ ᶻᵒⁿᵉ₃ 🌱

60 cm 90 cm 7

A favourite due to its golden leaves and upright habit. Quite sun tolerant if planted in a cool spot. Undemanding, but it prefers rich, well-drained soil. A winner!

Hosta 'Striptease'
'Striptease' Hosta

⬍ ⬌ ❀ ❀ ☁ ᶻᵒⁿᵉ₃ 🌱

50 cm 90 cm 7

Pale green foliage with a creamy white centre brought out by fine lines of pure white. Easy to grow and slug resistant. Plant it in rich, cool, well-drained soil.

Houttuynia cordata 'Chameleon'
Chameleon Plant

⬍ ⬌ ❀ ☀ ❀ ᶻᵒⁿᵉ₄

30 cm 40 cm 7-9

Very decorative as an edger around water gardens or in a pot in water gardens. Uniquely coloured foliage. Expands vigorously if planted in moist, rich soil.

Iris pallida 'Argentea Variegata'
Zebra Iris

⬍ ⬌ ❀ ❀ ᶻᵒⁿᵉ₄ 🌱 🪣 🦋

75 cm 40 cm 6

Irresistable flowers smelling like grape juice and striking variegated foliage make for a highly decorative plant both for the mixed border and along the edge of the water garden. Rich, cool, well-drained soil.

Iris sibirica 'Ausable River'
'Ausable River' Siberian Iris

🌡️ ↔️ ❄️ ☀️ 🌤️ ZONE 3

75 cm   40 cm   6-7

This disease and insect-resistant iris is perfect for the novice gardener. Tolerates a wide range of growing conditions, but prefers a spot with slightly acid, rich, cool, well-drained soil.

Iris versicolor
Blue Flag

🌡️ ↔️ ❄️ ☀️ ZONE 2

55 cm   40 cm   6-7

Beautiful native with charming flowers. For rich, heavy, slightly acid, and very moist soil. Interesting in drainage ditches.

Iris versata 'Gogo Boy'
'Gogo Boy' Versata Iris

🌡️ ↔️ ❄️ ☀️ 🌤️ ZONE 3

70 cm   30 cm   6-7

Superb blooms on very hardy, vigorous plants. Quebec hybrid that does best in rich, slightly acid and somewhat moist soil.

Lamiastrum galeobdolon 'Herman's Pride'
'Hermann's Pride' Yellow Archangel

Our favorite picks

🌡️ ↔️ ❄️ 🌤️ 🌥️ 🌿

30 cm   50 cm   5-6

The perfect groundcover for spots where "nothing will grow". Plant with decorative foliage, very tolerant to drought, heat and poor soils. Prefers rich, cool, well-drained soil.

Lamium maculatum 'Beacon Silver'
'Beacon Silver' Spotted Dead Nettle

🔼 ↔ ❀ ❁ ☁ ZONE 3 🦌

20 cm 50 cm 5-6

Good groundcover that loves rich, cool soil. Foliage almost entirely silvery white, a colour highly appreciated in the shade and at the base of trees and shrubs.

Lathyrus latifolius
Perennial Sweet Pea

🔼 ↔ ❀ ☀ ❁ ZONE 3

200 cm 40 cm 6-8

Pretty and vigorous climber to slip in here and there, among other perennials or to grow on a trellis. Likes rich, somewhat acid, cool, well-drained soil.

Lamium maculatum 'Pink Chablis'
'Pink Chablis' Spotted Dead Nettle

🔼 ↔ ❀ ☀ ❁ ☁ ZONE 4 🦌

20-30 cm 40 cm 5-6

Promising! A new variety with pink flowers, very useful as a groundcover in flower beds, but also grown in decorative containers. Prefers cool, rich, well-drained soil.

Lavandula angustifolia 'Munstead'
'Munstead' English Lavendar

🔼 ↔ ❀ ☀ ZONE 4 🦋

30-40 cm 30-50 cm 6-8

Always popular for its heady perfume. Compact variety that prefers moderately rich, light, dry soil. Tolerates drought once established.

Lavandula angustifolia 'Hidcote Blue'
'Hidcote Blue' English Lavendar

30 cm   30 cm   6-8

A heady perfume with Provençal overtones! Compact plant with narrow greyish foliage that tolerates dry soil, but prefers light, moderately rich ones. Plant in small clusters.

Lavandula angustifolia 'Hidcote Pink'
'Hidcote Pink' English Lavendar

30-45 cm   30-60 cm   6-8

Lovely narrow grey-tinted foliage that is very aromatic. Compact plant with pink flowers to plant in moderately rich, light, rather dry soil. Likes the heat.

Leucanthemum x *superbum* 'Becky'
(syn.: *Chrysanthemum maximum* 'Becky')
'Becky' Shasta Daisy

Our favorite picks

90 cm   60 cm   6-10

More and more popular, both because of its reliability and its abundant and long-lasting bloom. Grow in mass plantings in rich, cool, well-drained soil. Grows equally well in heavy and light soil.

Leucanthemum x *superbum* 'Silver Princess'
'Silver Princess' Shasta Daisy

(PV)

40 cm   40 cm   6-8

Dwarf variety and very floriferous. Grow it as an edging plant or in mass plantings in a flower bed. Plant in rich, light or heavy, cool, well-drained soil. Home gardeners love it!

Leucanthemum maximum 'Broadway Lights'
'Broadway Lights' Shasta Daisy

🌿 ↔ ❋ ☀ ☼ ZONE 4 🦋

45-60 cm   45 cm   7-8

Striking! Light yellow flowers turning cream as they age, creating a plant with subtle tones. Happy in rich, cool, well-drained soil. Tolerates both heavy and light soils.

Leucanthemum x superbum 'Alaska'
'Alaska' Shasta Daisy

🌿 ↔ ❋ ☀ ZONE 3 🦋

6 cm   30 cm   6-8

Beautiful large-flowered tall daisy. A classic! Ideal for mass plantings and flowerbed borders. Grow in rich, cool, well-drained soil.

Leucanthemum x superbum 'Sunny Side Up'
'Sunny Side Up' Shasta Daisy

New

🌿 ↔ ❋ ☀ ☼ ZONE 4 🦋

65-75 cm   30 cm   7-9

Huge semi-double flowers held up by rigid, strongly upright stems. Remove the faded flowers to prolong bloom. Interesting in small groups in mixed borders. Prefers rich, cool, well-drained soil.

Liatris spicata 'Kobold'
'Kobold' Blazing Star

PV

🌿 ↔ ❋ ☀ ☼ ZONE 3 🦋 🦌

45 cm   45 cm   7-9

Magnificent flowers on dense spikes on very easy-to-grow plants. It's a classic perennial border plant. This compact variety appreciates rich, acid, slightly moist soil.

Ligularia dentata 'Britt Marie Crawford'
'Britt Marie Crawford' Bigleaf Ligularia

(PV)

🌡 100-120 cm   ↔ 90 cm   ZONE 4   7-9

A future garden star! Huge rounded leaves are a very attractive deep burgundy. Golden yellow flowers rise well above them. Rich, slightly acid, somewhat moist soil.

Ligularia stenocephala 'Little Rocket'
'Little Rocket' Narrow Spiked Ligularia

🌡 50-60 cm   ↔ 40-60 cm   ZONE 4   8-9

It will be love at first sight! A dwarf version of the well-known ligularia, 'The Rocket', with the same toothed leaves and spectacular spiky blooms. It will be happy in slightly moist, rather rich, somewhat acid soil.

Ligularia dentata 'Othello'
'Othello' Bigleaf Ligularia

🌡 100-120 cm   ↔ 75-90 cm   ZONE 3   8-9

Beautiful and stately perennial with bronze leaves. Does best in the shady border. Always plant it in cool or slightly moist, rich, somewhat acid soil.

Lilium 'America'
'America' Asiatic Lily

🌡 90 cm   ↔ 45 cm   ZONE 3   7

Magnificent deep purple flower. Asiatic lilies are renowned for their beautiful blooms and their great vigour. Likes rich, slightly alkaline, cool, well-drained soil.

Lilium 'Stargazer'
'Stargazer' Oriental Lily

60 cm   45 cm   8

A strong fragance you'll notice from a distance! Huge and spectacular flowers, beautiful both in flower beds and bouquets. Prefers rich, very acid, cool, well-drained soil.

Lilium speciosum var. rubrum
Red Japanese Showy Lily

135 cm   35 cm   8-9

The perfect choice to steal the show in mixed perennial borders. Does best in rich, somewhat acid, cool, well-drained soil. Pleasing fragrance. Can also grow in containers.

Lobelia cardinalis
Cardinal Flower

90-120 cm   30 cm   7-9

Highly appreciated along streams, near water gardens or naturalized in slightly moist soil. Tolerates heavy soil, but prefers rich, slightly acid soil.

Lobelia x speciosa 'Fan' series
'Fan' Hybrid Lobelia

50-60 cm   30 cm   6-8

Collection of large-flowered, brilliantly coloured lobelia, some with dark purple foliage. Always a good choice for cool or slightly moist soil, ideally rich and somewhat acid.

Lupinus series 'Gallery'
'Gallery' Lupin

50 cm **40 cm** **6-7**

Spectacular in large masses! Prefers a cool climate where it naturalizes readily. Choose moderately rich, slightly acid, dry soil.

Lupinus 'Russel' series
'Russel' Lupin

90 cm **40 cm** **6-7**

Big floral spikes creating a wonderful effect when mass planted. Loves cool climates and cool, well-drained soil. Tall variety.

Lychnis arkwrightii 'Vesuvius'
'Vesuvius' Lychnis

45 cm **35 cm** **6-8**

Brilliant blossoms and slightly purple foliage. This lychnis looks great in mass plantings in borders with moderately rich, light soil.

Lychnis coronaria
Rose Campion

75 cm **45 cm** **7-8**

Pretty plant with brilliantly coloured, airy flowers. Self-sowing biennial. Good filler plant that tolerates poor, dry soil, but prefers moderately rich soil, light, cool, well-drained soil.

Lysimachia 'Snow Candle'
'Snow Candle' Loosestrife

30-45 cm 40 cm 6-9

Elegant pure white blooms on compact plants. Forms beautiful mass plantings under small trees and shrubs, in rich, somewhat acid, cool, well-drained soil. Tolerates dry soil once established.

Lysimachia punctata 'Alexander'
(syn.: *Lysimachia punctata* 'Variegata')
'Alexander' Yellow Loosetrife

60 cm 60 cm 6-7

Looks lovely in mass plantings with its creamy white leaf margins. The foliage takes on a beautiful pink tinge in the spring and fall. Plant in moderately rich, slightly acid soil, ideally evenly moist.

Lysimachia nummularia 'Aurea'
Golden Creeping Jenny

5 cm 45-60 cm 6-7

Creeping plant, ideal for decorating the edges of a water garden or planting among paving stones. Does well in moderately rich, slightly acid and rather moist soil.

Lythrum salicaria 'Robert'
'Robert' Purple Loosestrife

80 cm 45 cm 6-9

Floriferous beyond belief, this purple loosestrife produces deep pink flowers and its leaves take on lovely fall colours. Likes somewhat acid, slightly moist soil and moderately rich soil.

Lythrum 'Terra Nova'
'Terra Nova' Purple Loosestrife

PV

🔼 ↔ ❀ ☀ ❋ [ZONE 3] 🦋

55 cm 40 cm 7-9

Interesting selection due to its compact size and luminescent flowers. . Moderately rich, slightly acid, somewhat moist soil. Nearly sterile.

Malva sylvestris 'Zebrina'
Zebrina Common Mallow

Our favorite picks

🔼 ↔ ❀ ☀ [ZONE 3] 🦋

60-120 cm 50 cm 6-9

Easy to grow plant with uniquely coloured flowers. Vigorous, it forms beautiful mass plantings with other garden perennials. Grows equally well in alkaline or acid soil. Biennial that self sows.

Malva moschata 'Rosea'
Pink Muskmalllow

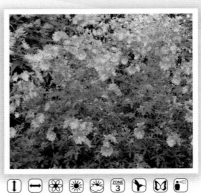

🔼 ↔ ❀ ☀ ❋ [ZONE 3] 🐦 🦋 💧

60 cm 60 cm 6-9

Gardeners love it because of its cottage garden look and its rock-solid nature. Very tolerant of different growing conditions, it prefers cool, well-drained, slightly alkaline and moderately rich soil.

Monarda 'Jacob Cline'
'Jacob Cline' Hybrid Beebalm

🔼 ↔ ❀ ☀ ❋ [ZONE 3] 🐦 🦋 💧 ✂

120 cm 60 cm 7-8

Tall variety with bright red flowers that is very mildew resistant. Grow in mass plantings in rich, moist soil.

Monarda 'Fireball'
'Fireball' Hybrid Beebalm

New

⬆ ↔ ✱ ☀ ❄ ZONE 4 🌿 🦋 📷 🚫
45-50 cm 30-40 cm 7-8

Large fire engine red flowers on compact plants more disease resistant that older varieties. Prefers rich, moist soil where it can be used as an edging plant. The flowers attract hummingbirds and make excellent cut flowers.

Monarda 'Petite Delight'
'Petite Delight' Hybrid Beebalm

Our favorite picks

⬆ ↔ ✱ ☀ ❄ ZONE 2 🌿 🦋 📷 🚫
45 cm 40 cm 7-8

A low-growing monarda that makes an excellent edging plant for flower beds. It does best in rich, moist soil. Quite disease-resistant. Always attractive.

Monarda didyma 'Coral Reef'
'Coral Reef' Hybrid Beebalm

New

⬆ ↔ ✱ ☀ ❄ ZONE 3 🌿 🦋 📷 🚫
90-120 cm 60-90 cm 7-8

Striking intense pink flowers on solid plants that are very disease resistant. Aromatic foliage and scented flowers that hummingbirds adore. Grow in rich, rather moist, well-drained soil.

Myosotis sylvatica 'Victoria' series
'Victoria' Woodland Forget-me-not

⬆ ↔ ✱ ☀ ❄ ☁ ZONE 3 🦋 🚫
15 cm 15-30 cm 5-6

Magnificient tiny sky blue flowers! Plant at the base of tulips or use to edge flower beds. Prefers cool soil, but also grows well in soil that is rich or poor, light or heavy. Self-sowing biennial.

Myosotis palustris
Water Forget-me-not

Our favorite picks

20 cm 25 cm 6-8

Take advantage of its beautiful spring bloom as an edging plant for the flower bed or in moist woodlands. Soil can be rich or poor, light or heavy, as forget-me-nots tolerate a wide range of conditions.

Oenothera macrocarpa (syn.: *O. missouriensis*)
Evening Primrose

20 cm 35 cm 6-9

Low-growing plant with very large flowers, ideal for edging in dry, light, poor soil. The flowers open at the end of the afternoon and close the next morning. Tolerates drought once established.

Oenothera fruticosa 'Fireworks'
'Fireworks' Sundrops

40 cm 60 cm 6-8

A vigorous perennial with bright yellow flowers and foliage that turns red in the fall. Ideal for beginners. Moderately rich, cool, well-drained soil.

Opuntia humifusa
Eastern Prickly Pear

Our favorite picks

30 cm 40 cm 6-7

A beavertail cactus that is perfectly hardy! Low-growing groundcover that prefers soil that is dry, light, and poor to moderately rich. Slow off the mark in spring.

Pachysandra terminalis
Japanese Pachysandra

20-30 cm   15-45 cm   5-6

An all-purpose groundcover that can grow just as well in deep shade under trees as in full sun. Tolerates poor soil and pollution, but it does prefer rich, very acid, well-drained soil.

Paeonia suffruticosa 'Ruffled Sunset'
'Ruffled Sunset' Tree Peony

100-150 cm   60 cm   6

Superb in every way. Insect and disease free, this peony bears flowers as colourful as a sunset. Plant in rich, cool, well-drained soil. Of limited hardiness.

Paeonia 'Bowl of Beauty'
'Bowl of Beauty' Peony

80 cm   65-80 cm   5-6

A beautiful once-blooming peony that deserves to be better known. Easy to grow. Plant it in rich, cool, well-drained soil.

Papaver nudicaule 'Champagne Bubbles'
'Champagne Bubbles' Iceland Poppy

45 cm   30 cm   7-9

Delicate flowers, larger than usual on this cultivar. It prefers rock gardens and alpine gardens with dry, moderately rich, well-drained, slightly alkaline soil. Self-sowing biennial.

Papaver orientale 'Beauty of Livermere'
'Beauty of Livermere' Oriental Poppy

90 cm   50 cm   5-6

You won't be able to garden without this poppy with dark red flowers! Tough, reliable and perfectly hardy, it grows in moderately rich, cool, well-drained soil. Prefers cool climates.

Penstemon digitalis 'Husker Red'
'Husker Red' Penstemon

85 cm   30 cm   6-7

Extended bloom that contrasts beautifully with the shiny dark purple foliage. Superb with 'Sprite' astible in slightly acid, moderately rich, well-drained soil.

Perovskia atriplicifolia
Russian Sage

Our favorite picks

90-120 cm   75 cm   ° 8-10

Pleasantly airy with its greyish, finely cut foliage and its tiny mauve flowers. It goes well with other perennials and loves poor, light, dry soil.

Persicaria amplexicaule 'Firetail'
'Firetail' Knotweed

Our favorite picks

70-100 cm   100-120 cm   6-7

Long blooming period and easy to grow. Vigorous, non invasive groundcover with upright blooms borne well above the foliage. Grows in rich, cool soil.

Phlox carolina 'Bill Baker'
'Bill Baker' Thickleaf Phlox

🔼 ↔ ❄ ☀ ❄ ZONE 3 🌿 🦋

50 cm 60 cm 6-8

Heavily blooming plant for use as an edging plant in flower beds or in rock gardens. Pest-free, this phlox grows in rich, slightly acid, cool, well-drained soil.

Phlox maculata 'Natascha'
'Natascha' Meadow Phlox

🔼 ↔ ❄ ☀ ZONE 3 🌿 🦋 🏷

90 cm 50 cm 6-8

Incredible biocolor flowers! This tall summer-blooming perennial is disease-resistant and loves rich, slightly moist soil. A plant worth discovering!

Phlox paniculata 'David'
'David' Garden Phox

🔼 ↔ ❄ ☀ ZONE 3 🌿 🦋 🏷

110 cm 60 cm 7-9

A very pretty phlox with white flowers, renowned for its excellent resistance to powdery mildew. For the back of the border in rich, cool, well-drained soil.

Phlox paniculata 'Starfire'
'Starfire' Garden Phox

🔼 ↔ ❄ ☀ ZONE 3 🌿 🦋 🏷

80 cm 50 cm 7-9

A classic of the mixed perennial border. Attractive, long-lasting blooms. Grow in small groups or mass plant in rich, cool, well-drained soil.

Phlox subulata 'Candy Stripe'
'Candy Stripe' Moss Phlox

15 cm   40 cm   5

A veritable cushion entirely covered with novel bicoloured flowers. An essential addtion to the flower bed, the rock garden or the border in rich, cool, well-drained soil.

Platycodon grandiflorus 'Sentimental Blue'
'Sentimental Blue' Balloon Flower

30 cm   40 cm   8-9

Remarkable! A very easy plant to grow, always beautiful. It produces large mauve flowers. Prefers rich, slightly acid, well-drained soil, but adapts to anything.

Polemonium caeruleum 'Bressingham Purple'
'Bressingham Purple' Jacob's Ladder

50 cm   40 cm   6-7

A beautiful bushy perennial with purplish foliage that harmonizes perfectly with the flowers. For rich, slightly moist, somewhat acid soil.

Polemonium caeruleum 'Snow and Sapphires'
'Snow and Sapphires' Jacob's Ladder

70 cm   60 cm   6-7

Remarkable plant with white-edged foliage, perfect for adding a special touch to the garden. Does especially well in slightly shady spots in rich and slightly moist soil.

Polygonatum multiflorum
Solomon's Seal

60 cm   30 cm   6-7

A flower of the woodland garden, with arched stems, it grows without difficulty even in the driest soil. It does prefer rich, slightly acid, cool, well-drained soil.

Primula denticulata
Drumstick Primrose

25 cm   15 cm   5-6

A tiny beauty of the spring garden with pretty globular flower heads. One of the most reliable primroses, it prefers rich, slightly acid and slightly moist soil.

Primula polyantha 'Pacific Giant Hybrids'
'Pacific Giant Hybrids' English Primrose

25 cm   20 cm   5-6

Perfect for adding colour to somewhat shady gardens, especially in rich, slightly acid and slightly moist soil. Plant here and there in small clusters.

Pulmonaria longifolia ssp. *cevennensis*
Longleaf Lungwort

30 cm   45 cm   5-6

Give your flower beds a look of distinction thanks to this plant with narrow, dark green, white-spotted leaves and intense blue flowers. Prefers rich, cool, well-drained soil.

Pulmonaria saccharata 'Mrs Moon'
'Mrs Moon' Lungwort

🌡 30 cm ↔ 45 cm 5-6 ❀ ❂ ☁ ZONE 3 ✂

Magnificent spring blooms that go from pink to mauve to dark blue. Green leaves spotted white. Plant in cool, rich, well-drained soil. Popular!

Pulsatilla vulgaris
Pasque Flower

Our favorite picks

🌡 15-25 cm ↔ 30 cm 4-5 ❀ ❂ ☁ ZONE 3 ✂

A must for the rock garden, with its downy foliage and its over-sized flowers. Loves moderately rich soil, light, slightly alkaline, cool, well-drained soil.

Rodgersia aesculifolia
Fingerleaf Rodgersia

Our favorite picks

🌡 80 cm ↔ 40-60 cm 7-8 ❀ ❂ ☁ ZONE 4

A remarkable plant thanks to its textured leaves softly tinged bronze. Useful in shade in rich, acid, slightly moist soil.

Rudbeckia fulgida 'Goldsturm'
'Goldsturm' Coneflower

🌡 70 cm ↔ 50 cm 7-9 ❀ ❂ ZONE 3

Very popular and beloved by gardeners. Easy to grow, it thrives in a wide range of conditions, including dry, poor, and heavy soils. Floriferous!

Rudbeckia triloba
Three-lobed Coneflower

🔧 ↔ ❄ ☀ ❉ ZONE 3 🦌 🦋 ✂

125 cm 90 cm 8-9

A very tall perennial that produces hundreds of golden yellow flowers. Beautiful in wildflower gardens where it attracts butterflies and birds. Plant in moderately rich, slightly moist soil.

Salvia nemerosa 'Marcus'
'Marcus' Meadow Sage

Our favorite picks

🔧 ↔ ❄ ☀ ❉ ZONE 4 🦌 🦋 🪴

25 cm 45 cm 6-8

One of the most interesting perennials for gardens with dry soil. Even with no irrigation, it produces its beautiful deep blue flowers. Prefers moderately rich, cool, moist soil.

Salvia pratensis 'Rose Rhapsody'
'Rose Rhapsody' Meadow Clary

New

🔧 ↔ ❄ ☀ ❉ ZONE 5 🪴 ✂

45-60 cm 30-45 cm 7-9

Very floriferous, 'Rose Rhapsody' blooms non-stop until fall. Its beautiful flower stalks look perfect in a cottage garden, preferably in moderately rich, cool, well-drained soil.

Scabiosa columbaria 'Butterfly Blue'
'Butterfly Blue' Scabious

🔧 ↔ ❄ ☀ ZONE 5 🦌 🦋

45 cm 45 cm 7-8

With its delicate, romantic appearance, this floriferous, very hardy perennial prefers moderately rich, cool, moist soil. It tolerates dry soil and slightly alkaline soil. Perfect for the rock garden.

Sedum 'Picolette'
'Picolette' Sedum

New

30-45 cm 30 cm 8-9

Charming fall bloomer. Foliage in a thousand shades of black, purple, and dark brown topped off by numerous masses of carmine pink flowers. Undemanding, it prefers moderately rich, well-drained soil.

Sedum telephium 'Black Jack'
(syn.: *Hylotelephium* 'Black Jack')
'Black Jack' Sedum

Our favorite picks

45-60 cm 45-60 cm 8-10

Nearly black, the foliage of 'Black Jack' contrasts with all its neighbours. Easy to grow, undemanding, it prefers moderately rich, well-drained soil.

Sedum telephium 'Matrona'
'Matrona' Fall Sedum

45-60 cm 45-60 cm 8-10

Superb fall-bloomer, grown for its foliage that is tinted grey or purple, depending on the season. Loves moderately rich, cool, moist soil, but tolerates poor, dry soil as well.

Sedum reflexum 'Angelina'
'Angelina' Sedum

PV

15 cm 20-45 cm 6-7

Unusual! A vigorous groundcover with foliage that is yellow in the spring, chartreuse green in the summer, and bright red in the fall. To top it off, it grows well in poor, stony, dry soils!

Sedum telephium 'Autumn Joy'
'Autumn Joy' Fall Sedum

🔲 60 cm 🔲 60 cm 🔲 8-10 ☀️ ZONE 2 🔲 🔲

A classic perennial for the novice gardener. Beloved for its ease of care and its beautiful blooms that attract butterflies. Prefers moderately rich, well-drained soil.

Sedum spurium 'Dragon's Blood'
'Dragon's Blood' Two-row Stonecrop

🔲 15 cm 🔲 30 cm 🔲 7-8 ☀️ 🔲 ZONE 3 🔲

A tough plant that is very much at ease in the rock garden or as an edging plant in light, dry soil where it carpets the ground with its unique foliage.

Sedum spathulifolium 'Cape Blanco'
'Cape Blanco' Broadleaf Stonecrop

🔲 10 cm 🔲 50 cm 🔲 6-7 ☀️ 🔲 ZONE 4 🔲

Small but spectacular with its blue-green foliage and its bright yellow flowers. Will really stand out in a trough or rock garden in poor, stony, dry soil.

Sempervivum 'Red Beauty'
'Red Beauty' Hens and Chicks

🔲 10 cm 🔲 15 cm 🔲 7 ☀️ 🔲 ZONE 3

Always interesting in decorative containers, in trough gardens, between the stones of a rock garden or in the cracks of walls. Loves poor, stony, dry soil.

Sidalcea 'Party Girl'
'Party Girl' Checker Mallow

⬍ ⬌ ✿ ☀ ❄ ZONE 5 🦅 🦋

75 cm 45 cm 7-8

An upright plant with brilliant bloom. Remarkable in the mixed border in rich, slightly moist soil.

Stachys monnieri 'Hummelo'
Hummelo' Alpine Betony

⬍ ⬌ ✿ ☀ ❄ ZONE 4 🦋

50 cm 50 cm 6-7

Unique and different! Abundant bloom. For use as an edging plant for mixed borders. Prefers poor, light, cool, well-drained soil.

Thymus pseudolanuginosus
Woolly Thyme

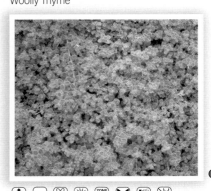

⬍ ⬌ ✿ ☀ ZONE 3 🦋 🌡 ✗

5 cm 40 cm 6-7

A very low-growing groundcover with downy foliage, perfect for spaces between flagstones or for edging paths. Does best in light, moderately rich, cool, well-drained soil.

Thymus serpyllum 'Coccineus'
Creeping Red Thyme

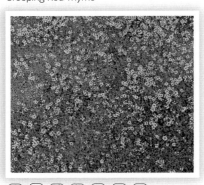

⬍ ⬌ ✿ ☀ ZONE 3 🦋 🌡

15 cm 35 cm 6-8

A plant that rapidly carpets the ground, both in the sun and under shrubs. Plant in moderately rich, light, dry soil.

Tiarella cordifolia 'Iron Butterfly'
'Iron Butterfly' Foamflower

30 cm   30 cm   5-6
Dramatic! A collector's plant for the woodland garden with beautiful, deeply divided foliage marked in the middle with a nearly black spot. For rich, somewhat acid, slightly moist soil.

Tradescantia andersoniana 'Blue and Gold'
'Blue and Gold' Spiderwort

50 cm   40 cm   6-9
Electrifying golden yellow foliage that contrasts with purple flowers. It does best protected from full sun in rich, slightly moist, somewhat acid soil.

Tricyrtis hirta 'Miyazaki'
'Miyazaki' Toad Lily

90 cm   45 cm   9-10
An original touch for the shade garden with its arched stems and purple-spotted lilac blooms. Grows in rich, slightly acid, cool soil.

Trollius 'Golden Queen'
'Golden Queen' Globe Flower

75 cm   45 cm   5-6
Beautiful blooms at the very beginning of summer just when the tulips are at their peak. This waterhog prefers rich, slightly acid soil.

Veronica spicata 'Royal Candles'
'Royal Candles' Spike Speedwell

(PV)

45 cm   60 cm   6-8

Pure beauty in the garden! This must-have for the mixed border goes with pratically everything. Generally undemanding, it nevertheless prefers light, slightly acid, dry soil.

Veronica spicata 'Giles van Hees'
'Giles van Hees' Spike Speedwell

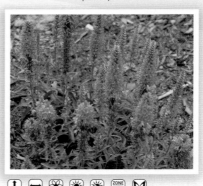

20 cm   20 cm   7-9

A veritable butterfly magnet that flowers over and over again. Compact plant for moderately rich soil, light, dry soil.

Veronicastrum virginicum 'Fascination'
'Fascination' Culver's Root

120-150 cm   100 cm   7-9

A tall, stately plant with impressive flowers. Useful for the back of the border in rich, cool, well-drained soil. A natural for country gardens.

Vinca minor
Periwinkle

15 cm   30-60 cm   5-6

A vigorous groundcover with evergreen leaves and sky blue flowers in spring. It adores rich, cool conditions, but will also grow in dry, acid or heavy soil.

Vinca minor 'Atropurpurea'
Purple-flowered Periwinkle

🔲 ↔ ❄ ☀ ❄ ☁ [ZONE 4] 🚫
15 cm 30-45 cm 5-6

Surprising flowers almost burgundy in colour against shiny dark green leaves. The perfect groundcover under conifers, even though it prefers rich, cool, well-drained soil.

Viola corsica
Corsican Viola

🔲 ↔ ❄ ☀ ❄ ☁ [ZONE 5]
20 cm 20 cm 5-9

Always in bloom, this viola is easy to fit into flower beds and decorative containers. It also naturalises in lawns. Grows in rich, cool, well-drained soil.

Viola 'Rebecca'
'Rebecca' Viola

🔲 ↔ ❄ ☀ ❄ ☁ [ZONE 5] 🪴
20 cm 20 cm 5-9

Each fragrant flower is different in colour, but they are all irresistible. Adds colour to the shade garden in rich, cool, well-drained soil.

Viola labradorica 'Purpurea'
Purple Labrador Violet

🔲 ↔ ❄ ☀ ❄ ☁ [ZONE 3]
10 cm 20 cm 5-9

The purple foliage is just as beautiful as the tiny flowers! Ideal for mass plantings out of the full sun in rich, slightly acid, well-drained soil. Self sows.

Annuals

Annuals are little treasures that fill our surroundings with colours and sunlight! Each spring, they call to us from their trays and other containers with their variety of choices. Even if your fingers itch to pick up one tray of each, it's important to understand that their colours will be participating in the landscape of your beds and pots for a long season. So take a few seconds to recall the colours of your landscape so that you won't be tempted to choose the wrong shades! Annuals will be part of your landscape for months at a time, so if you remember to include them as the full-fledged members they really are, they'll repay you handsomely!

Choosing the right annuals is as simple as continuing the colour scheme you've already chosen. That way the design will be strong and more striking and there'll be no colour conflicts. Also, quantities are unlimited. One good design trick is to repeat in containers the same annuals you've planted in the ground. This repetition will bring harmony to the rest of your landscape. And don't forget the tall annuals that you can buy in pots or ready to sow: they are perfect for inserting among other plants. It's an easy and pleasant way of enriching your flowerbeds!

◀ *Rudbeckia hirta* 'Prairie Sun'

Annuals | 107

Abutilon x hybridum series 'Bella'
'Bella' Flowering Maple

35-45 cm 30-45 cm 5-9

Huge brightly coloured flowers on a compact, heat-tolerant plant. Perfect for giving an exotic look to decorative containers and flowering borders. Flowers over a long period in moderately rich, moist soil.

Alyssum maritima series 'Wonderland'
(syn.: *Lobularia maritima* série 'Wonderland')
'Wonderland' Sweet Alyssum

10 cm 20 cm 5-9

Well known to gardeners, it forms dense cushions of bloom. Useful in decorative containers, but also as an edging plant in moderately rich, well-drained soil.

Ageratum houstonianum series 'High Tide'
'High Tide' Flossflower

35-45 cm 25 cm 5-9

Performs better in a garden setting than the other flossflowers. More drought tolerant. Flowers abundantly. Tall variety that needs little care. Prefers moderately rich, moist soil.

Amaranthus tricolor 'Early Splendor'
'Early Splendor' Joseph's Coat

90 cm 60 cm

Grown for its magnificent bright red leaves that turn deep violet as they age. Upright growth and very easy to grow. Grows very well in light, dry soil.

Angelonia angustifolia 'Serena' series
'Serena' Angelonia

Our favorite picks

25-30 cm   30 cm   5-10

Perfect annual for the gardener looking for something new. Very reliable, floriferous, and easy to grow. A pest-free plant. Grows in moderately rich, cool, well-drained soil.

Antirrhinum majus
Snapdragon

20-90 cm   15-30 cm   6-10

Highly appreciated for its brilliantly coloured flowers shaped like a dragon's mouth. Interesting in mass plantings, mixed plantings, and containers. Prefers rich, cool, well-drained soil.

Argyranthemum frutescens 'Butterfly'
'Butterfly' Paris Daisy

45-90 cm   30 cm   5-10

Always in bloom and very dainty. Perfect plant for container gardening, alone or with other flowers. Prefers relatively rich, cool, well-drained soil. A must!

Begonia semperflorens
Wax Begonia

20 cm   20 cm   5-9

A classic that grows as well in shade as in full sun. Looks good in mass plantings, flower beds, and containers. Perfect too for filling in small spaces. Prefers rich moist soil.

Begonia x *hybrida* 'Dragon Wing'
'Dragon Wing' Begonia

30-40 cm 30-45 cm 6-9

Popular with gardeners, this begonia with drooping flowers really shines when grown in a container. The flowers are accompanied by magnificent shiny dark green foliage. Plant in rich, cool, well-drained soil.

Begonia x *tuberhybrida*
Tuberous Begonia

30 cm 30 cm 5-9

Easy to grow and available in a wide range of colours, these begonias are always spectacular. Perfect for container gardening, you can also grow them in flower beds in rich, cool, well-drained soil.

Begonia x *tuberhybrida* Non Stop 'Mocca Orange'
'Non Stop Mocca Orange' Tuberous Begonia

25 cm 25 cm 5-9

A striking contrast! Variety with dark bronze, almost chocolate foliage and double flowers in hot colours. Unbeatable in containers and flowerboxes or as an edging plant in rich, cool, well-drained soil.

Begonia x *tuberhybrida* series 'Illumination'
'Illumination' Tuberous Begonia

30 cm 60 cm 5-9

Charming plant with a weeping habit, perfect for hanging baskets and containers. Brilliantly coloured annual that is also easy to grow. Grows best in rich, cool, well-drained soil.

Bidens ferulifolia 'Peter's Gold Carpet'
'Peter's Gold Carpet' Tickseed

20 cm 40 cm 5-9

Good companion plant with brilliant and abundant bloom. Nothing better for filling hanging baskets and decorative containers, in moderately rich, cool, well-drained soil.

Browallia speciosa
Bush Violet

15-30 cm 15-25 cm 6-9

Beautiful starry flowers on bushy plants, for use in in-ground mass plantings in light shade. Also very pretty in containers in sun as long as the soil remains slightly moist at all times.

Brassica oleracea 'Redbor'
'Redbor' Ornamental Kale

45-60 cm 45 cm

Celebrate the end of the season with this unparalleled plant. It's actually a kale with very curly burgundy foliage that takes on a beautiful red coloration in the fall. Plant in slightly moist soil. Edible foliage.

Brugmansia arborea
Angel's Trumpet

100-150 cm 90-120 cm 5-9

Stunning plant with large trumpet-shaped hanging flowers. Highly fragrant, especially at nightfall. A good choice for the sunny patio. Likes rich, cool, well-drained soil.

Calibrachoa 'Callie' series
'Callie' Calibrachoa

15-25cm   50cm   5-10

Masses of small flowers on slightly trailing plants. Rich in colour, this annual gives life to hanging baskets and decorative containers. Like its cousin the petunia, it should be planted in rich, cool, well-drained soil.

Calibrachoa 'Superbells' series
'Superbells' Calibrachoa

25cm   60cm   5-10

Magnificent bloom… and it flowers from spring right through fall. Flowers a bit bigger than other calibrachoas on hanging plants : perfect for hanging baskets. Grows in rich, cool, well-drained soil.

Canna x *generalis*
Canna

200cm   30-50cm   7-10

Give your garden an exotic look with this stately plant offering both decorative foliage and striking flowers. Looks good with both annuals and perennials. Especially likes rich soil.

Capsicum annuum 'Black Pearl'
'Black Pearl' Ornamental Pepper

35cm   30cm   6-9

With its deep purple foliage, this pepper with ornamental fruit just as dark is perfect for enhancing annuals in decorative containers. A charmer that is heat resistant and prefers rich, slightly moist soil.

Capsicum annuum 'Garda Tricolor'
'Garda Tricolor' Ornamental Pepper

25 cm   25 cm   6-9

A striking mix of yellow, scarlet red, and purple fruits…
all on the same plant! Alone or in clusters, this ornamental
pepper will seduce you. Recommended for rich, slightly
moist soil. Very heat resistant.

Celosia argentea plumosa 'Fresh Look Gold'
'Fresh Look Gold' Feather Celosia

New

35 cm   30 cm   5-10

Remarkable annual due to its long blooming period and
highly coloured flowers. It will grow in heat in dry soil.
Although reliable under all conditions, celosias still prefers
rich, cool, well-drained soil. AAS 2007 winner.

Catharanthus rosea 'Pacifica Burgundy Halo'
'Pacifica Burgundy Halo' Madagascar Periwinkle

25-35 cm   15-20 cm   5-9

AAS 2007 winner. A compact and floriferous annual that
is becoming very popular. Its coloured flowers against dark
green, shiny foliage are unique. Likes rich, slightly moist soil.
Drought resistant.

Cleome hassleriana 'Queen' series
'Queen' Spiderflower

90-125 cm   50 cm   5-10

A tall, very easy to grow variety with aromatic leaves and
flowers. Ideal for the back of the border. Grows well in light,
cool, well-drained soil.

Coleus scutellarioides 'Kong' series
(syn.: *Solenostemon scutellarioides* série 'Kong')
'Kong' Coleus

Our favorite picks

30-45 cm   25-50 cm

Huge decorative leaves, ideal for adding colour to the shade garden or as a companion for mixed annuals in containers. Likes rich, slightly moist soil.

Coleus scutellarioides 'Fishnet Stocking'
(*Solenostemon scutellarioides* 'Fishnet Stocking')
'Fishnet' Coleus

New

45-60 cm   30-45 cm

No two leaves are identical. A mix of dark burgundy veins over green leaves. Large-leaved annual, interesting in containers or mass plantings. For all types of soil.

Coleus scutellarioides 'Wizard' series
(syn.: *Solenostemon scutellarioides* 'Wizard' series)
'Wizard' Coleus

20 cm   20 cm

Multipurpose plant that grows as well in decorative containers as in large beds or borders. Short variety available in many colours. For all.

Colocasia esculenta 'Illustris'
'Illustris' Taro

120 cm   45 cm

Exotic foliage that combines green and deep purple to create a most interesting effect. Perfect for moist soil and shady spots.

Cordyline indivisa
Dracaena

45-120 cm   45-75 cm

A classic accent plant for containers and flower beds thanks to its narrow, arching leaves. Plant in moderately rich, slightly moist soil.

Cosmos bipinnatus 'Sonata' series
'Sonata' Cosmos

45-60 cm   30-40 cm   6-10

Compact, very floriferous variety that looks just as good in flower beds as in containers. The large flowers grow very well in poor, dry soil.

Cordyline terminalis 'Maroon Magic'
'Maroon Magic' Dracena

45-120 cm   45-75 cm

The magnificent dark maroon foliage gives a contemporary feel to all decorative containers. Likes moderately rich, slightly moist soil.

Dahlia 'Hello!' series
'Hello!' Dahlia

25 cm   15 cm   6-10

Big double flowers in bright colours on small, compact plants. Useful for brightening up decorative containers, but also very pretty in beds. Good in rich, cool, well-drained soil.

Dahlia x *hybrida*
Dahlia

60-150 cm 45-60 cm 6-10

Blooms non stop from the end of the summer until frost. A huge range of flower colours, shapes, and sizes. Likes rich, cool, well-drained soil.

Diascia barberae 'Diamonte' series
'Diamonte' Twinspur

25-30 cm 25-30 cm 6-9

Spiffs up hanging baskets and mixed plantings. Looks good mixed with snapdragons and China pinks. Likes moderately rich, cool, well-drained soil.

Dianthus 'Ideal Violet'
'Ideal Violet' China Pink

25-30 cm 20-25 cm 5-10

The beautiful fringed flowers with their rich coloration look marvellous in flower beds along with perennials and annuals. Grows in moderately rich, cool, well-drained soil. Named an All-America Classic.

Dichondra argentea 'Silver Falls'
Silver Falls

New

10-20 cm 60-150 cm

Recommended in hanging baskets and decorative containers because of its trailing habit. The round, silvery leaves are always beautiful. Undemanding, it prefers moderately rich, rather dry soil, light soil.

Euphorbia hypericifolia 'Diamond Frost'
'Diamond Frost' Euphorbia

30-45 cm   40 cm   5-10

An explosion of tiny, airy white flowers. The ideal filler plant for flowerboxes and decorative containers. Blooms all summer. Heat and drought tolerant. Named an "Exceptional Plant" in 2007 in the Daniel A. Séguin Garden.

Fuchsia x *hybrida*
Fuchsia

30-60 cm   30-60 cm   5-9

Exceptional flowers on upright or trailing plants. Perfect for containers situated out of the wind and sun in moderately rich, slightly moist soil.

Gaura lindheimeri 'Stratosphere' series
'Stratosphere' Gaura

30-40 cm   25 cm   5-10

Delicate flowers borne on tall arching stems that look great with other annuals. Drought and heat resistant. Grows equally well in poor and rich soils, but it does require good drainage

Gazania splendens
Gazania

20-30 cm   15-20 cm   5-9

Heat tolerant, the flowers open in the day and close at night. Perfect for poor, slightly acid, dry soil.

Gerbera 'Giant Spinner'
'Giant Spinner' Gerbera

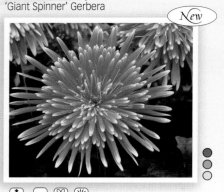

☝ 30-45 cm ↔ 30 cm ✿ 6-9 ☀

Immense, brightly coloured, very double flowers. To bloom well, this annual requires rich soil that is always slightly moist. Interesting in beds and in containers.

Gerbera jamesonii 'Festival' series
'Festival' Gerbera

☝ 30-35 cm ↔ 20-25 cm ✿ 6-9 ☀ ✉

Huge, very colourful flowers looking like giant daisies. Needs rich soil that is always slightly moist.

Hedera helix
English Ivy

☝ 15 cm ↔ 80 cm ☀ ✿ ⬮

Give a distinguished look to containers thanks to the graceful stems and beautiful leaves of English ivy. Also used as a groundcover in sun and shade in moderately rich, cool, well-drained soil.

Helianthus annuus
Sunflower

☝ 30-250 cm ↔ 25-60 cm ✿ 6-9 ☀ ⚘

Tall or short, sunflowers are always a delight. Grow these waterhogs in small masses in moderately rich, cool, well-drained soil.

Bracteantha bracteata (syn. *Helychrysum bracteathum*)
Everlasting

30-45 cm 25 cm 6-10

Pretty flowers with a papery texture, very popular in dried flower bouquets. Also interesting massed together and mixed with other annuals. Grows in poor, dry soil.

Heliotropium arborescens
Heliotrope

30-60 cm 25-40 cm 5-10

Flowers with a sumptuous scent of vanilla. Grows readily in decorative containers or in beds. Heat tolerant. Grows in moderately rich, cool, well-drained soil.

Helichrysum petiolare
Licorice-Plant

20-30 cm 35-50 cm

A plant with ornamental foliage that always brings out the best in neighbouring flowering plants, both in containers and flower beds. Grows equally well in poor or moderately rich soils.

Hibiscus moscheutos 'Luna' series
Hibiscus

60-90 cm 60 cm 6-9

Immense beautifully coloured flowers on compact plants that love heat and sun. Truly impressive, it prefers rich moist soils.

Impatiens walleriana 'Xtreme' series
Impatiens

25 cm   25 cm   5-9

How could we get through the summer without this classic annual, always in bloom, even in the densest shade? Very easy to grow, impatiens prefers rich, cool, slightly moist soil.

Impatiens 'Sonic' series
'Sonic' New Guinea Impatiens

30 cm   25 cm   5-9

Multi-purpose, floriferous annual that grows equally well in decorative containers and in flower beds. It likes rich, cool, slightly moist soil.

Ipomoea batatas
Sweet Potato

30 cm   120 cm

Decorative leaves and trailing stems, an ideal filler plant along with flowering annuals, for hanging baskets. Tolerates poor soil, but prefers cool, well-drained soil.

Iresine 'Purple Lady'
'Purple Lady' Iresine

New

30 cm   75 cm

It trails, it crawls, it spreads. The ornamental foliage is just what you need to accompany blooming annuals in decorative containers or for a great groundcover in cool, poor, slightly acid soil.

Lamiastrum galeobdolon (syn. *Lamium galeobdolon*)
Yellow Archangel

⊡ ⊟ ❀ ☀ ♼

30 cm   30-45 cm   6

Beautiful foliage companion plant for annuals in hanging baskets and decorative containers. Happy in rich, cool, well-drained soil.

Lantana camara 'Morning Glow' series
'Morning Glow' Lantana

⊡ ⊟ ❀ ☀ ❀ 🦋

30-75 cm   25-45 cm   5-10

The bicolour flowers are true butterfly magnets! Bushy plants that are very floriferous when grown in rich, somewhat acid, slightly moist soil.

Leucanthemum 'Broadway Lights'
'Broadway Lights' Shasta Daisy

⊡ ⊟ ❀ ☀

45-60 cm   30 cm   5-8

Daisy lovers will be thrilled with this butter yellow variety. Adapts well to heavy soil, but needs rich, cool, well-drained soil.

Lobelia erinus 'Blue Star'
'Blue Star' Edging Lobelia

New

⊡ ⊟ ❀ ☀ ❀ ▨

10 cm   15-20 cm   5-10

Pretty trailing companion plant with larger flowers than other edging lobelias. Beautiful all season if grown in rich moist soil.

Lysimachia nummularia
Creeping Jenny

10 cm 40-60 cm 6-7

Beautiful round leaves that trail from hanging baskets and containers. Grows in more or less rich, slightly moist soil.

Nemesia 'Sunsatia' series
'Sunsatia' Nemesia

25-35 cm 20-30 cm 5-9

Hugely popular mixed with other annuals in hanging baskets. Grows also in decorative containers and flowerboxes in rich, cool, well-drained soil.

Nicotiana 'Perfume Deep Purple'
'Perfume Deep Purple' Nicotiana

40-50 cm 30 cm 5-10

With its sweet perfume, this workhorse of a plant is able to flower abundantly in both poor, dry soils and rich, slightly moist ones.

Nierembergia hippomanica 'Mont Blanc'
'Mont Blanc' Cupflower

15 cm 25 cm 5-10

Always in bloom, this bushy annual with fine foliage loves rich, cool, well-drained soil. It's ideal for decorative containers but grows also in beds.

Oryza sativa 'Black Madras'
'Black Madras' Ornamental Rice

New

40 cm   30 cm

This ornamental rice plant is a grass with green leaves stained purple. Recommended for slightly moist, moderately rich soil.

Osteospermum 'Nuanza Copper Purple'
'Nuanza Copper Purple' Osteospermum

New

30-45 cm   45 cm   5-9

Large flowers in incomparable colours. The plant with a rounded habit is ideal in cool, moderately rich, well-drained soil. Use as an accent plant in the ground or in containers.

Osteospermum 'Symphony' series
'Symphony' Osteospermum

Our favorite picks

25-35 cm   25 cm   5-9

Uniquely coloured flowers. This annual is more floriferous that the other osteospermums. Prefers cool, moderately rich, well-drained soil.

Oxalis vulcanicola 'Red Wine'
'Red Wine' Shamrock

15 cm   15 cm   5-10

Remarkable foliage tinged red and dark purple. Superb companion plant in decorative containers. Likes rich, slightly moist soil.

Pelargonium peltatum 'Mini Cascade' series
'Mini Cascade' Ivy Geranium

PV

☐ ☐ ☐ ☐ ☐
15 cm 30 cm 5-10

Irreplaceable in hanging baskets, this trailing annual is very floriferous and compact. Very fond of fertilizer, it grows in cool, well-drained soil.

Pelargonium 'Patriot' series
'Patriot' Zonal Geranium

PV

☐ ☐ ☐ ☐ ☐
30 cm 25 cm 5-10

Easy to grow, this geranium is a classic flower bed plant for moderately rich, well-drained soil. Also perfect for decorative containers.

Pelargonium peltatum 'Global' series
'Global' Ivy Geranium

☐ ☐ ☐ ☐ ☐
25 cm 50 cm 5-10

Always in bloom, this series offers large, semi-double flowers in unique shades. Trailing plant, ideal for decorating window ledges. Loves fertilizer and cool, well-drained soil.

Petunia x *hybrida* 'Ultra Crimson Star'
'Ultra Crimson Star' Petunia

☐ ☐ ☐ ☐ ☐
30 cm 30 cm 5-9

Named an All-America Classic thanks to its bicolor flowers with a wavy margin and its compact habit. Use in flower beds in moderately rich, cool, well-drained soil.

Petunia hybrida 'Supertunia' series
'Supertunia' Petunia

25 cm   35 cm   5-9

Always in bloom, fragrant, vigorous and heat resistant. A winner requiring almost no maintenance for use in big hanging baskets and as a filler plant for flower beds in cool, well-drained soil.

Petunia 'Wave Purple'
'Wave Purple' Petunia

Our favorite picks

20 cm   120 cm   5-10

Spectacular! This creeping annual covers itself in purple flowers to the great pleasure of home gardeners. Likes cool, well-drained soil. Named an All-America Classic.

Plectranthus forsteri 'Variegatus'
Variegated plectranthus

20 cm   80 cm

Magnificent variegated aromatic foliage that goes well with flowering annuals in decorative containers and hanging baskets. Drought tolerant.

Portulaca grandiflora 'Sundial' series
'Sundial' Portulaca

20 cm   20 cm   5-10

Creeping plant ideal for dry, poor, hot soil, where it grows readily. Large brilliantly coloured flowers on thick leaves.

Ricinus communis
Castor Bean Plant

100-150 cm 100 cm

Give your flower beds in rich, slightly moist soil an exotic look thanks to this statuesque plant covered in giant leaves usually purplish in colour.

Rudbeckia hirta 'Indian Summer'
'Indian Summer' Black-Eyed Susan

PV

100 cm 35 cm 7-10

Always a favourite. A vigorous, solid plant for the flower bed where it creates a dazzling show. Grows in poor or rich, light or heavy, slightly moist soil.

Rudbeckia hirta 'Irish Spring'
'Irish Spring' Black-Eyed Susan

New

80 cm 45 cm 7-10

Big yellow flowers with a green cone. Blooms continuously until frost. Undemanding, it grows in poor or rich, light or heavy, slightly moist soil. Winner of an "Exceptional Plant" award at the Daniel A. Séguin Garden.

Rudbeckia hirta 'Prairie Sun'
'Prairie Sun' Black-Eyed Susan

Our favorite picks

70 cm 35 cm 7-10

Sunny, floriferous plant that grows equally well in poor or rich, light or heavy, slightly moist soil. Grow in beds but also in decorative containers.

Rudbeckia hirta 'Toto' series
'Toto' Black-Eyed Susan

30-40 cm 15-20 cm 7-10

Just as pretty in decorative containers as in flower beds, this annual tolerates poor or rich, light or heavy soils, but prefers slightly moist conditions.

Salvia farinacea 'Evolution'
'Evolution' Mealy Sage

35-50 cm 35 cm 5-10

Unbeatable plant for its easy care, its drought resistance and its generous and intense flowering. Grow in containers or in flower beds, preferably in moderately rich, cool, well-drained soil.

Salvia splendens 'Dancing Flame'
'Dancing Flame' Salvia

New

60 cm 30-45 cm 5-10

This salvia will certainly attract attention not only through its brilliant red flowers, but also through its yellow spotted foliage. It creates striking masses of colour in moderately rich, cool, well-drained soil.

Scaevola aemula 'Saphira Blue'
'Saphira Blue' Fan Flower

Our favorite picks

20 cm 45 cm 5-9

Spectacular in hanging baskets and decorative containers. Grow alone or mix with other annuals. Prefers rich, cool, well-drained soil.

Senecio cineraria
Dusty Miller

(PV)

20 cm   20 cm

Heat and drought-resistant, it's a good choice for adding a touch of contrast to decorative containers or to create formal edging in flower beds.

Senecio mikanioides
German Ivy

15 cm   80 cm

Always appreciated for the touch of fresh green it adds to hanging baskets and decorative containers. It grows best in moderately rich, cool, well-drained soil.

Solanum jasminoides
Star of Bethlehem

20 cm   120 cm   6-9

Filler plant with long arching stems and small star-shaped flowers. Grows well in poor, cool, well-drained soil.

Sutera cordata
Bacopa

Our **favorite** *picks*

15 cm   25 cm   5-9

Delicate companion plant with tiny flowers. Trails nicely from hanging baskets and containers. Good in slightly moist soil.

Tagetes patula
French Marigold

25 cm 20 cm 5-10

Very popular for its ease of growth and its continuous bloom. Heat- and drought-tolerant, it gets along with very little, but does prefer moderately rich, cool, well-drained soil.

Torenia 'Summer Wave' series
'Summer Wave' Trailing Wishbone Flower

20 cm 30 cm 5-10

A must for the shade garden. Slightly trailing, it does best in rich moist soils. Ideal for flowerboxes.

Tropaeolum majus
Nasturtium

30-40 cm 30 cm 6-9

With its edible leaves and flowers, it is the perfect annual for decorating the vegetable garden. Does fine even in poor soil, but prefers cool, well-drained soil.

Verbena bonariensis
Brazilian Verbena

120 cm 40 cm 7-10

More and more popular, this tall delicate-looking annual is adapted to flower beds in poor, stony, dry soil. Butterfly magnet!

Verbena rigida 'Polaris'
'Polaris' Verbena

New

🔼 ↔ ❄ ☀ 🦋 ✂
30-45 cm 25 cm 6-9

Delicate and romantic. The globe-shaped flower heads add lightness to any mixed planting, whether in containers or in poor, stony, dry soil. It looks like a miniature Brazilian verbena.

Verbena 'Lanai' series
'Lanai' Verbena

🔼 ↔ ❄ ☀ ❄ ☁ 🦋 ✂
20 cm 60 cm 5-9

Charming trailing variety with flowers in vibrant colours, ideal for hanging baskets and containers. Loves rich, cool, well-drained soil.

Vinca major
Greater Periwinkle

🔼 ↔ ☀ ❄
10-25 cm 150 cm

Magnificent trailing foliage. Perfect for decorating hanging baskets and containers. Requires cool, well-drained soil and tolerates poor soil, but will not tolerate drought.

Viola 'Majestic Giants Mix'
'Majestic Giants Mix' Pansy

🔼 ↔ ❄ ❄ ☁
15 cm 15 cm 5-10

Named an All-America Classic. Huge flowers in every possible colour add a note of elegance to containers and to flower beds. Pansies prefer cool temperatures and rich soil.

Zinnia Profusion 'Deep Apricot'
'Profusion Deep Apricot' Zinnia

New

30 cm 25 cm 5-10

Zinnia with a unique coloration, named an "Exceptional Plant" by the Daniel A. Séguin Garden. Generous bloom on a very tough and easy to grow plant. Grow in beds or in borders in moderately rich, well-drained soil. Tolerates dry soil.

Zinnia elegans 'Uproar Rose'
'Uproar Rose' Zinnia

Our favorite picks

75-90 cm 40-60 cm 6-10

Very popular with gardeners. Impeccable and generous blooms that make very beautiful cut flowers. Attractive both in decorative containers and in beds, in moderately rich, rather dry soil.

Zinnia Profusion 'Cherry'
'Profusion Cherry' Zinnia

PV

30 cm 25 cm 5-10

Expect a floral explosion from this easy-to-grow, disease-free annual. Makes fabulous mass plantings and uniform edges. Tolerates dry soils and grows best in moderately rich soil.

Zinnia elegans 'Zowie! Yellow Flame'
'Zowie! Yellow Flame' Zinnia

60-90 cm 40-70 cm

Wow! A very colourful bloom that will certainly grab everyone's attention! Plant in small groups in flower beds, in moderately rich, rather dry soil, for a very colourful effect!

Vines

Clematis hybride

Vines are quite amazing, actually.
You'll enjoy watching them reach for the sky! They have the curious habit of being able to cling to surfaces, either with twining stems or special twisting stems called tendrils that wrap around branches or trellises or, thanks to aerial roots or suction pads, climb up walls. You may want to adopt a vine to decorate a wall like a living tapestry or to cover latticework fixed around a patio. On small lots, adding a climber to a wall gives it greater depth and creates a feeling of well-being. Some climbing plants can also cover pergolas and reduce the effect of the sun's heat: no need to cram together under a parasol. Most often vines are used to cover vertical surfaces, but they can also be used as groundcovers, notably over vast areas that are difficult to reach, such as a steep slope. No matter where you put them, vines always add refinement to the landscape as well as pretty flowers or shiny, refreshing leaves.

Clematis macropetala 'White wings'

Actinidia kolomikta 'Arctic Beauty'
'Arctic Beauty' Hardy Kiwi

⬍ 5,00 m   ⬌ 3,00 m   ❋ 5   ☀ ☼ ❄ ⌁ ZONE 4 ▣

Brightly coloured, tricolour foliage that covers a huge surface with very little care. This vigorous plant likes rich, somewhat acid, cool, well-drained soil. Twining stems.

Akebia quinata
Chocolate Vine

⬍ 6,00-10,00 m   ⬌ 3,00-6,00 m   5   ❋ ☀ ☼ ❄ ⌁ ZONE 5 ▣

Should be grown more often in gardens. Very hardy, vigorous, with beautiful foliage on twining stems. Will even grow in shade. For moderately rich, well-drained soil.

Ampelopsis brevipedunculata 'Elegans'
Porcelain Berry

Our favorite *picks*

⬍ 3,00-7,00 m   ⬌ 1,00-3,00 m   ☀ ❄ ⌁ ZONE 5 ⚘

Grow it for the form and speckled coloration of its foliage, but also for its pink-tinted stems. Plant in moderately rich, cool, well-drained soil. Clings using tendrils.

Aristolochia macrophylla (syn.: *Aristolochia durior*)
Dutchman's Pipe

Our favorite *picks*

⬍ 5,00 m   ⬌ 2,00-3,00 m   6-7   ❋ ☼ ⌁ ZONE 4 ☙ ⚘

Its twining stems create a true green wall in no time. Tidy foliage covers a plant that does well in rich, cool, well-drained soil.

Campsis radicans
Trumpet Creeper

3,00-5,00 m 2,00-3,00 m 7-9 ZONE 5

An exotic looking plant with beautiful, brilliantly coloured, trumpet-shaped blossoms. Grows in all types of soil: poor, rich, dry, moist, heavy, light, acid or alkaline.

Celastrus orbiculatus 'Hercules'
'Hercules' Oriental Bittersweet

10,00 m 2,00 m 6 ZONE 2

Male plant to grow with 'Diana' in order to obtain berries. Like 'Diana', but without berries. Moderately rich, somewhat acid, cool, well-drained soil.

Celastrus orbiculatus 'Diana'
'Diana' Oriental Bittersweet

10,00 m 2,00 m 6 ZONE 2

Very vigorous plant, able to hide undesirable views in the garden. Beautiful berries in the fall. Plant with 'Hercules' in moderately rich, somewhat acid, cool, well-drained soil.

Clematis 'Comtesse de Bouchaud'
'Comtesse de Bouchaud' Clematis

4,00 m 2,00-3,00 m 7-9 ZONE 3

Big pink flowers that will bring colour to sunny trellises. All large-flowered clematis need cool, well-drained and rather rich soil.

Clematis 'Elsa Späth'
'Elsa Späth' Clematis

2,00 m 1,50 m 5-9

Always a favourite with big mid-blue flowers and dark purple stamens. Needs cool and well-drained, rather rich soil. Climbs using twining stems.

Clematis 'Jackmanii'
'Jackmanii' Clematis

4,00-6,00 m 3,00 m 7-9

The best known and most popular clematis, with its big intense purple blooms. Plant in cool, well-drained and rich soil.

Clematis 'Jackmanii Superba'
'Jackmanii Superba' Clematis

4,00 m 3,00 m 7-9

Like dark purple velvet! Superb and abundant bloom. Plant with twisting petioles that will grow in rich, cool, well-drained soil.

Clematis 'Josephine'
'Josephine' Clematis

2,00-3,00 m 1,50 m 6-9

Spectacular double flowers much sought after by gardeners. Accent plant for rich, cool, well-drained soil. Prune lightly early in spring.

Clematis 'Nelly Moser'
'Nelly Moser' Clematis

$\updownarrow$ 2,00-3,00 m $\;\;\leftrightarrow$ 1,50 m $\;\;$ 7-9 $\;\;$ ☀ $\;\;$ ☼ $\;\;$ ZONE 4

Generous! Big bicolour flowers appreciated for their originality. Like the saying goes, "clematis like their head in the sun and their feet in the shade." Rich, well-drained soil.

Clematis 'Rouge Cardinal'
'Red Cardinal' Clematis

$\updownarrow$ 2,50 m $\;\;\leftrightarrow$ 1,50 m $\;\;$ 7-9 $\;\;$ ☀ $\;\;$ ☼ $\;\;$ ZONE 4

Rather unusual colour for a large-flowered clematis. Interesting when grown with white or purple clematis in rich, cool, well-drained soil.

Clematis 'Piilu'
'Piilu' Clematis

Our favorite picks

$\updownarrow$ 2,00-3,00 m $\;\;\leftrightarrow$ 2,00 m $\;\;$ 7-9 $\;\;$ ☀ $\;\;$ ☼ $\;\;$ ZONE 4

Beautiful, spectacular, original! Somewhat smaller flowers with wavy petals, sometimes double, but always numerous. Prune lightly in spring. Cool soil.

Clematis tangutica 'Golden Tiara'
(syn.: *C. tangutica* 'Kugotia')
'Golden Tiara' Golden Clematis

$\updownarrow$ 3,00 m $\;\;\leftrightarrow$ 2,00 m $\;\;$ 7-9 $\;\;$ ☀ $\;\;$ ☼ $\;\;$ ZONE 3 $\;\;$ ❧

Very easy to grow, this clematis bears hanging yellow flowers larger than those of the species. Prefers moderately rich, cool, well-drained and slightly alkaline soil.

Clematis 'Ville de Lyon'
'Ville de Lyon' Clematis

2,00-3,00 m 1,50 m ❀ ☀ ❁ ZONE 4 7-9

Proudly displays its beautiful very dark pink flowers with a rounded outline. Plant in rich, cool and well-drained soil with a climbing rose like 'John Cabot'.

Humulus lupulus 'Aurea'
Golden Hops

6,00 m 1,50 m ☀ ❁ ZONE 4

Create intimacy by letting hops cover your patio's treillises. Twining stems regrow from the ground each spring. Likes rich, cool, well-drained soil. Very undemanding.

Hydrangea petiolaris
Climbing Hydrangea

Our *favorite* *picks*

8,00 m 3,00 m ❀ ☀ ❁ ⬡ ZONE 5 6-7

Very beautiful but slow-growing climber that clings to surfaces thanks to adhesive roots. For moderately rich, light, somewhat acid and well-drained soil.

Lonicera 'Mandarin'
'Mandarin' Climbing Honeysuckle

4,00 m 2,00 m ❀ ☀ ❁ ZONE 4 6-7

Flowers in unique colours that drive hummingbirds wild. Disease-free, this climbing honeysuckle does best in moderately rich, cool, well-drained soil.

Parthenocissus quinquefolia
Virginia Creeper

(PV)

7,00-15,00 m 5,00-10,00 m ZONE 2

The most vigorous of all climbing plants. It covers entire walls by clinging to surfaces with its tendrils. Moderately rich, light or heavy, slightly moist soil. Beautiful fall colours.

Parthenocissus quinquefolia 'Star Showers'
'Star Showers' Virginia Creeper

Our favorite picks

4,00-6,00 m 4,00 m ZONE 4

Very pretty foliage spotted green and creamy white. Can be used on a wall or as a groundcover. For a slightly moist, somewhat acid, light or heavy soil. Beautiful fall colours.

Parthenocissus quinquefolia var. engelmannii
Engelmann Virginia Creeper

8,00-15,00 m 5,00-8,00 m ZONE 2

Like the usual Virginia creeper, but with smaller leaves that turn bright red in the fall. Undemanding, it prefers moderately rich, somewhat acid, slightly moist soil.

Parthenocissus tricuspidata 'Golden Wall'
'Golden Wall' Boston Ivy

5,00 m 3,00 m ZONE 4

Illuminate trellises with the beautiful golden leaves that keep their coloration throughout the entire summer. Tolerates all types of soil, including poor, light, heavy, acid and alkaline.

Polygonum aubertii (syn.: *Fallopia aubertii*)
Chinese Fleecevine

[↕] [↔] [✹] [☀] [❄] [ZONE 5]

4,00 m   2,00 m   8-9

Delicate creamy white flowers on a spreading climbing plant that resprouts from the base each spring. Tolerates dry soil and adapts to different conditions.

Vitis riparia
Riverbank Grape

(PV)

[↕] [↔] [✹] [☀] [☁] [ZONE 2] [🐦]

6,00-10,00 m   2,00-5,00 m

Native plant ideally suited to the natural garden in moderately rich, light to heavy, slightly moist soil. Edible fruits and beautifully coloured fall foliage.

Wisteria floribunda 'Lawrence'
'Lawrence' Japanese Wisteria

[↕] [↔] [✹] [☀] [❄] [ZONE 4] [▮] [✕]

3,50 m   2,00 m   6

Spectacular bloom that doesn't occur every year, but is a treat for the eyes when it does appear. Plant in a protected spot in moderately rich, cool, well-drained soil.

Aristolochia gigantea (annual)
Brazilian Dutchman's Pipe

[↕] [↔] [✹] [☀]

2,50 m   1,00 m   6-8

One of the weirdest flowers that exists. Climber with twining stems, grown as a curiosity. Requires lots of fertilizer and rich, cool, well-drained soil.

Asarina scandens
Climbing Snapdragon

3,00 m 1,50 m 5-9

Small climber always in bloom from spring through fall. Does best in container gardens. Enjoys rich, cool, well-drained soil.

Cobaea scandens
Cup and Saucer Vine

(PV)

3,00 m 2,00 m 7-9

It will cling to any surface by the tips of its leaves, which are transformed into tendrils. Fertilize only lightly for best bloom. Plant in rich, slightly moist soil.

Ipomoea quamoclit
Cypress Vine

2,00 m 1,20 m 6-9

Fine foliage looking like fir needles. Scarlet flowers somewhat different from those of its cousin, the morning glory. Happy in light, moderately rich, cool, well-drained soil.

Ipomoea tricolor
Morning Glory

3,00 m 1,00 m 6-9

Continuous bloom, with flowers that open early in the morning. The stems will wrap around trellises, stakes or taut strings. Fertilize little and grow in moderately rich, light, dry soil.

Lablab purpureus (syn.: *Dolichus purpureus*)
Hyacinth Bean

3,00 m 2,00 m 7-9

A close cousin of the garden bean with slightly purple foliage, bright pink flowers, and flat purple seed pods. Moderately rich, somewhat acid, slightly moist soil.

Lathyrus odoratus
Sweet Pea

1,50-3,00 m 0,60-1,00 m 7-8

The sweet pea gets its name from the intoxicating scent of the flowers. Plant it once and you'll never want to be without it again. Rich, well-drained soil.

Mandevilla sanderi
Mandevilla

1,00 - 2,00 m 0,70 m 6-9

Decorate your garden with this floriferous plant. Since it tolerates dry soil, it does best in container gardens. Prefers moderately rich, cool, well-drained soil.

Mina lobata
Spanish Flag

2,00 - 4,00 m 1,00 m 7-9

Often grown in containers for its intriguing clusters of bicolour flowers. In the ground, give it moderately rich, cool, well-drained soil.

Passiflora caerulea
Passionflower

⬍ 1,50-5,00 m ⬌ 1,00 m ❀ 7-9 ☀ ☼

Very complex and very beautiful flowers. Likes frequent watering. Grow in moderately rich, cool, well-drained soil.

Rhodochiton atrosanguineum
Purple Bell Vine

⬍ 2,00 m ⬌ 1,00 m ❀ 6-9 ☀ ☼

Pretty climbing plant with hanging flowers. Ideal for growing over metal arches. Transplant with care into moderately rich, cool, well-drained soil.

Thunbergia alata
Black-eyed Susan Vine

(PV)

⬍ 1,50-2,00 m ⬌ 0,75 m ❀ 6-9 ☀ ☼

Very pretty alone or with other annuals in a hanging basket. Grow in the ground in rich, somewhat acid, cool, well-drained soil. Water regularly.

Thunbergia 'African Sunset'
'African Sunset' Black-eyed Susan Vine

⬍ 1,50-2,00 m ⬌ 0,75 m ❀ 6-9 ☀ ☼

New variety in shades of peach, a gradation that goes from apricot to brick red. Likes rich, somewhat acid, cool, well-drained soil. Also for containers.

Ornamental
Grasses

Hakonechloa macra 'Aureola'

More and more present

in landscaping, ornamental grasses create quite a stir… and no wonder! Their long, graceful stems that dance in the slightest breeze are always fascinating to watch and their fluffy flower spikes, short or tall, end the season with a bang. Ornamental grasses recall the vast plains where their ancestors still dominate the landscape. It's a bit of this spirit of liberty that makes grasses what they are. A wide range of heights, textures, and colours add to their list of qualities and when they're in a group, their movement creates quite an effect!

Most ornamental grasses like open spaces and full sun; they often adapt well to drought. On the other hand, there are other grasses that prefer partial shade and moister growing conditions. Ask the experts at Passion Jardins to show you the ones best adapted to your yard and to calculate the quantities you'll need to give a "back on the farm" look to your landscape.

Pennisetum sp.

Pennisetum secatum 'Rubrum'

Arrhenatherum elatius 'Variegatum'
Variegated Bulbous Oatgrass

Our favorite picks

30 cm   20 cm

Beautifully striped foliage for use in mass plantings on the edge of or near the waater garden. Plant in moderately rich, light, somewhat acid, cool, well-drained soil. Vigorous.

Bouteloua gracilis
Blue Grama

30 cm   20 cm

Strange inflorescences that grow sideways on a docile plant that likes poor, rocky, dry and somewhat alkaline soil.

Calamagrostis x acutiflora 'Karl Foerster'
'Karl Foerster' Feather Reed Grass

Our favorite picks

150-170 cm   50-75 cm

Very upright grass. A favourite that tolerates dry or poor soil, but prefers rich, acid or alkaline, cool, well-drained soil.

Calamagrostis x acutiflora 'Overdam'
'Overdam' Feather Reed Grass

120 cm   50-75 cm

Robust variety with narrow variegated leaves. Very decorative. Plant as a specimen plant in rich, acid or alkaline, cool, well-drained soil.

Calamagrostis brachytricha
Korean Feather Reed Grass

100-150 cm   50 cm

Superb pinkish flower spikes that are both airy and robust. Grows in rich, somewhat alkaline, cool, well-drained soil. Tolerates both dry and moist soil. Very decorative!

Carex flacca (syn.: *C. glauca*)
Blue Sedge

25 cm   30 cm

Magnificent masses of narrow leaves tinged metallic blue. A good edging plant for the shade garden. Undemanding, this sedge does well in moderately rich, moist soil.

Carex morrowii 'Ice Dance'
'Ice Dance' Japanese Sedge

30 cm   45 cm

Tall sedge with narrow leaves bearing a fine cream margin. Plant in large masses under trees in rich, somewhat acid, moist soil.

Carex testacea
Orange-bronze Sedge

100 cm   20 cm

Absolutely unique! Fine leaves tipped in bright orange. A striking contrast to annuals with purple flowers, like heliotrope or mealy sage. Moderately rich, cool, well-drained soil.

Chasmanthium latifolium
Northern Sea Oats

70-100 cm   40 cm

Grass with an oriental appearance thanks to its wide leaves arching at the tip. Its blooms in small, flat, hanging spikes take on golden shades in the fall. Needs rich, cool, well-drained soil.

Deschampsia cespitosa 'Bronzeschleier'
'Bronzeschleier' Tufted Hairgrass

100 cm   60 cm

Beautiful native deserving of more interest! Airy blooms that bend gracefully at the tip. Tolerates all soils but dry ones.

Cortaderia selloana
Pampas Grass

200 cm   75-90 cm

Tall and impressive. Superb feathery silver blooms. Mulch heavily in winter. Likes moderately rich, well-drained soils.

Deschampsia cespitosa 'Northern Lights'
'Northern Lights' Tufted Hairgrass

New

35-40 cm   50 cm

One of the prettiest variegated foliages that exist with hints of gold, cream, pink, and purple, depending on the season. Tolerant of a wide range of growing conditions, it does prefer cool, well-drained and moderately rich soil.

Eragrostis 'Wind Dancer'
'Wind Dancer' Love Grass

Our favorite picks

115 cm   135 cm

Fine textured grass with an airy, light bloom. Bluish leaves. Plant in small groups along flower beds in moderately rich, cool, well-drained soil.

Festuca glauca 'Elijah Blue'
'Elijah Blue' Blue Fescue

20 cm   30 cm

The bluest of all the blue fescues! Fine leaves forming a dense tuft, even in poor, rocky, somewhat acid, dry soil.

Hakonechloa macra 'Aureola'
Variegated Japanese Forest Grass

Our favorite picks

35 cm   30 cm

The essential touch to any small garden of oriental inspiration. Slow-growing plant that does well in rich, heavy, slightly acid, cool, well-drained soil.

Helictotrichon sempervirens
(syn.: *Avena sempervirens*)
Blue Oat Grass

80 cm   40 cm

Fine blue-green, spiky foliage. The perfect plant for difficult conditions like poor, rocky, dry soil. Indifferent to pH.

Isolepis cernua 'Live Wire'
'Live Wire' Fibre Optic Grass

New

15-20 cm 25-50 cm

Add texture to your mixed containers with this fine-leaved annual grass. Its novel blooms recall fibre optic threads! Remains beautiful from spring through fall. Well adapted to moist soil.

Miscanthus sinensis 'Malepartus'
'Malepartus' Maiden Grass

200 cm 100 cm

Immense grass that can be used as a screen or to hide undesirable views. Happy in rich and somewhat moist soil. Foliage turns coppery in fall.

Miscanthus sinensis 'Huron Sunrise'
'Huron Sunrise' Maiden Grass

150 cm 150 cm

Stately plant, unbeatable for its generous bloom slightly tinted burgundy. Radiant in rich, slightly moist soil.

Miscanthus 'Purpurascens'
Purple Maiden Grass

PV

175 cm 90 cm

Stands out from the other maiden grasses due to its beautiful reddish coloration in the fall. Vigorous, it tolerates the worst conditions, including poor, heavy or light, dry soil.

Miscanthus sinensis 'Silberfeder'
'Silberfeder' Maiden Grass

Our favorite picks

220 cm   150 cm

A tall variety with silvery blooms which starts to flower in August. Perfect for the back of flower beds in rich, slightly moist soil. Decorative even in winter!

Panicum 'Prairie Fire'
'Prairie Fire' Switchgrass

New

120-150 cm   60-75 cm

Promising variety with its bluish leaves in spring turning to deep red in summer. Light flower spikes tinted pink add to its charm. Grows in rich, light or heavy soil, dry to moist soil. Slow to come up in spring.

Molinia caerulea 'Skyracer'
'Skyracer' Purple Moor Grass

180-225 cm   100 cm

Like a fireworks display! Tall flower stems are borne well above the narrow foliage. Very airy blooms. Adapts to rich, very acid, cool, well-drained soil.

Panicum virgatum 'Prairie Sky'
'Prairie Sky' Switchgrass

120 cm   50 cm

A switchgrass with leaves as blue as the sky! Easy to grow. Plant with echinaceas in rich, light or heavy soil, dry to moist soil. Slow to come up in spring.

Panicum virgatum 'Shenandoah'
'Shenandoah' Switchgrass

100 cm   40 cm

The tips of the leaves turn red in summer and the whole plant turns burgundy in fall. As well adapted to heavy soils as light ones and to dry soils as moist ones.

Pennisetum setaceum 'Rubrum'
Purple Fountain Grass

75-100 cm   45-60 cm

Narrow purple leaves and delicate, arching flower spikes. Adds colour to decorative containers or plant with perennials in rather poor, cool, well-drained soil.

Pennisetum glaucum 'Purple Baron'
'Purple Baron' Ornamental Millet

75-115 cm   60 cm

Just as impressive as its cousin, 'Purple Majesty', but shorter, so it is more appropriate in home gardens. Prefers rather poor, cool, well-drained soil.

Phalaris arundinacea 'Feesey's Form'
'Feesey's Form' Ribbon Grass

60 cm   50 cm

Very vigorous, but oh so pretty! White variegated leaves shaded pink in spring and fall. Tolerates all soils, but prefers rich, somewhat acid, moist ones.

Sesleria autumnalis
Autumn Moor Grass

45 cm 40 cm

Small grass with chartreuse foliage that grows very well in poor, rocky, dry soil. An edging plant for flower beds. Pest-free.

Sorghastrum nutans 'Sioux Blue'
'Sioux Blue' Indian Grass

180 cm 75 cm

Grass with a very vertical habit and blue-green leaves. Decorative in winter. Plant in poor or rich, light or heavy, cool, well-drained soil.

Spartina pectinata 'Aureomarginata'
Variegated Prairie Cordgrass

150 cm 75 cm

Ribbons of grass lined in cream on a plant able to colonize ditches or create a grass screen around water gardens. It tolerates light to heavy, dry to very moist soil.

Stipa tenuissima
Feather Grass

Our favorite picks

60 cm 30 cm

Very fine foliage creating an attractive show in containers or in the company of other grasses. Tolerates poor, light, heavy, dry soil.

Ferns

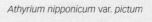

As soon at the sun's rays become stronger, ferns unroll under our feet as if by magic. Their elegant fronds stretch out then arch outward, giving us the typical silhouette we know so well. They evoke coolness and grace and when we see them by the hundreds in our forests, we're quickly charmed. Ferns live in colonies, spreading in tight formation. They therefore have to be grouped together to grow well and to create an image of movement. Most ferns prefer a moist, humid environment out of the wind and it is important to replicate those conditions if you want a fern bed in your yard.

Canada has many genera of native ferns from similar natural environments. They are normally used in cool, shady locations and, since they are used to feeding from the abundant leaf litter for forests, they're also quite greedy in the garden! An application of good leaf compost each fall will help them thrive. Daffodils and small spring bulbs are ideal companions for fern beds. What a spring show you'll have!

Matteucia struthiopteris

Adiantum pedatum
Northern Maidenhair

50 cm	50 cm			ZONE 3	

The most beautiful of our native ferns. Delicate fronds held horizontally. Beautiful as an edging plant along paths. For moderately rich, slightly acid and somewhat moist soil.

Asplenium trichomanes 'Incisum'
Incised Maidenhair Spleenwort

20 cm	20 cm			ZONE 3	

Ideal for cracks in shady stone retaining walls. Loves growing vertically in slightly alkaline rock faces. Evergreen foliage.

Athyrium 'Branford Rambler'
'Branford Rambler' Fern

75 cm	75 cm			ZONE 4	

Beautiful in woodlands in rich, somewhat acid, slightly moist soil. Also good along stream edges. Tolerates drier soil.

Athyrium filix-femina 'Cristatum'
Crested Lady Fern

45 cm	45 cm			ZONE 5	

The curious narrow, extremely divided fronds criss-cross. Unique! Plant in small groups in rich, somewhat moist, slightly acid soil.

Athyrium filix-femina 'Lady in Red'
'Lady in Red' Lady Fern

60-80 cm   60-75 cm

Just as fascinating through its airy foliage as its bright red petioles. Plant in rich, somewhat acid, slightly moist soil. Tolerates dense shade.

Athyrium nipponicum var. pictum
Japanese Painted Fern

50 cm   30 cm

A real treasure with fronds marked in grey and mauve. Use as an accent plant. Prefers rich, slightly moist soil. Pour dense shade.

Athyrium filix-femina 'Plumosum Axminster'
'Plumosum Axminster' Crested Lady Fern

Our favorite picks

60-80 cm   60 cm

Very original with its deeply divided foliage making it appear quite frizzy. A beautiful apple green that mixes well with hostas and other ferns. Rich, somewhat acid moist soil.

Athyrium nipponicum 'Burgundy Lace'
'Burgundy Lace' Painted Fern

45 cm   30 cm

You'll never be able to get along without this wonderful fern with grey and burgundy fronds that will even grow in dense shade. Likes rich and somewhat moist soil.

Dryopteris erythrosora 'Brilliance'
'Brilliance' Autumn Fern

Our favorite picks

⬍	⬌	☀	⛅	ZONE
60 cm	45 cm			5

Very beautiful orange and bronze coloration in the young fronds. Maintains some of its colour throughout the summer. Plant it where the soil is rich, acid and somewhat moist.

Matteuccia struthiopteris
Ostrich Fern

⬍	⬌	☀	⛅	ZONE	🦌
100 cm	80 cm			3	

Tall fern that forms colonies over time. Prefers a slightly shady spot in rich moist soil but tolerates dry, acid or poor soil.

Osmunda cinnamonea
Cinnamon Fern

Our favorite picks

⬍	⬌	☀	☀	⛅	ZONE	🦌
60-100 cm	30-80 cm				3	

Easy fern that produces cinnamon-coloured fertile fronds in the centre of its rosette of always attractive sterile fronds. Tolerates heavy, very acid, dry or moist soil.

Osmunda regalis
Royal Fern

PV

⬍	⬌	☀	☀	⛅	ZONE	🦌
120 cm	90 cm				3	

Very large fern bearing fronds with rounded tips. Beautiful in group plantings. Will grow in full sun if planted in water, but will tolerate very dry soil if grown in shade. Also good for acid, rich or heavy soil.

Trees

Liriodendron tulipifera 'Aureomarginatum'

There is no doubt that trees are the mainstay of our environment.
Without them, seasons are almost all alike and space is empty. Trees are very important for our environment and our first reflex when we start creating a new landscape is to plant trees, as many as possible. With their arching branches and their verdant foliage, they protect us from the ever harsher rays of the sun while creating ever moving patterns of shade that are both pleasant and refreshing! They support life as well, that of birds and beneficial insects, and they bring a fundamental structure to any space even as they frame our homes. Trees never hide the house, instead, they highlight it.

Magnolia sp.

That's why a house with trees around it always sells for more than a house that has none. Let the experts at **Passion Jardins** garden centres guide you in choosing the best trees for your environment.

Don't delay, plant trees today!

Acer x freemanii 'Autumn Blaze'
'Autumn Blaze' Freeman Maple

The most beautiful of all trees grown for fall colours: it turns completely red! Undemanding tree that does well in rich, somewhat alkaline, cool, well-drained soil.

15,00 m 12,00 m ZONE 4

Acer ginnala
Amur Maple

Small tree very interesting for city gardens. Tolerant of pollution and de-icing salt, it will grow in moderately rich, rather dry soil. Tolerates heavy or light soil.

7,00 m 6,00 m ZONE 2 6

Acer platanoides 'Princeton Gold'
'Princeton Gold' Norway Maple

Sparkling leaves that keep their yellow coloration all summer. Very resistant to burning sun and to both heavy and light soils. Plant in rich, cool and well-drained soil.

12,00 m 10,00 m 5 ZONE 4

Acer platanoides 'Royal Red'
'Royal Red' Norway Maple

The most beautiful selection, with deep purple leaves in summer. Grows readily in heavy or light soil, but prefers rich, cool, well-drained soil.

15,00 m 10,00 m 5 ZONE 4

Acer rubrum
Red Maple

Native tree with spectacular fall colours. Very hardy, it grows in slightly moist, somewhat acid, rich soil.

20,00 m 16,00 m 5 ZONE 3

Acer saccharum
Sugar Maple

Native tree well known for the maple syrup it produces. Red and orange foliage in the fall. Likes rich, cool, well-drained, slightly acid soil.

25,00 m 15,00 m ZONE 4

Aesculus glabra
Ohio Buckeye

Blooms in long spikes appear at the same time lilacs are in flower. Palmate leaves and spineless fruit. Rich, somewhat acid, cool, well-drained soil.

Our favorite picks

15,00 m 7,00 m 6 ZONE 3

Amelanchier canadensis
Shadblow Serviceberry

Always beautiful! White flowers in spring, edible berries in summer, orange leaves in fall, and grey bark in winter. Adapts to any soil.

7,00 m 3,00 m 5 ZONE 3

Betula nigra 'Heritage'
'Heritage' River Birch

Superb bark with a pinkish tinge; it exfoliates even more than the bark of paper birch! This birch grows in heavy, slightly acid, moist soil. Resistant to bronze birch borer.

⬍ 15,00 m   ⬌ 10,00 m   ☀ ❄ ZONE 5

Caragana arborescens 'Pendula'
Weeping Peashrub

Small grafted tree with weeping branches. Very hardy. Decorative even in windy spots whether the soil is poor or rich, light or dry.

⬍ 2,00 m   ⬌ 2,00 m   5   ☀ ❄ ZONE 2

Caragana arborescens 'Walker'
'Walker' Weeping Peashrub

Fine foliage and very weeping habit. Perfect for beautifying small spaces. Grafted plant that does equally well in poor soil as rich. Likes light, dry soil.

⬍ 2,50 m   ⬌ 1,50 m   5   ☀ ❄ ZONE 2

Celtis occidentalis
Common Hackberry

Native tree that tolerates heat, drought, wind, and alkaline soils. Tough plant that does well in rich and somewhat moist soil.

⬍ 10,00 m   ⬌ 8,00 m   ☀ ❄ ZONE 3

Crataegus x mordenensis 'Toba'
'Toba' Hawthorn

Small tree with double
flowers and fruits that
last into late fall.
Drought-resistant, it
grows in all types of soil.

5,00 m 3,00 m 5-6 ZONE 3

Euonymus alatus 'Compactus'
Dwarf Burning Bush Standard

Rounded, compact shrub
grafted onto a solid trunk.
Bright red fall foliage on a
tough pest-resistant
plant. Very tolerant of all
soil types.

2,00 m 1,20 m ZONE 4

Fraxinus americana 'Autumn Purple'
'Autumn Purple' White Ash

Unique deep purple fall
colour while other ashes
usually turn yellow at
that season. Rich,
somewhat acid, cool,
well-drained soil.
Tolerates moist soil.

Our favorite picks

16,00 m 7,00 m ZONE 3

Fraxinus excelsior 'Pendula'
Weeping Ash

A large weeping tree that
is both attractive and very
tough. Vigorous and
inspiring. Plant in rich,
cool, well-drained soil.

4,00 m 4,00 m ZONE 5

Fraxinus nigra 'Fallgold'
'Fallgold' Black Ash

Dark green summer
leaves that turn golden
yellow in fall. Good city
tree that tolerates poor,
heavy, very acid, moist
soil.

18,00 m 12,00 m

Ginkgo biloba
Maidenhair Tree

The most resistant of all
trees with unique leaves
that turn golden yellow in
the fall. Slow growing.
Prefers light, poor or rich,
acid or alkaline, cool and
well-drained soil.

20,00 m 10,00 m

Gleditsia triacanthos 'Prairie Silk'
'Prairie Silk' Thornless Honeylocust

Gives light shade and
thus allows you to
garden at its base. Fine
foliage on very horizontal
branches. Likes moder-
ately rich, light, cool,
well-drained soil.

9,00 m 6,00 m

Gleditsia triacanthos 'Sunburst'
'Sunburst' Thornless Honeylocust

New growth is coloured
bright yellow. Striking
deeply cut foliage on a
tree that does well in
moderately rich, light,
cool, well-drained soil.

12,00 m 16,00 m

Hydrangea paniculata 'Grandiflora'
Peegee Hydrangea Standard

A classic offering spectacular end-of-summer bloom. Grafted plant that forms a small tree useful in landscaping. Best in rich, slightly moist soil.

4,00 m   2,00 m   7-9   ZONE 3

Hydrangea paniculata 'Unique'
'Unique' Panicle Hydrangea Standard

This beautiful top-grafted hydrangea has delicate flowers. An accent plant with a rounded habit, ideal in rich, slightly moist soil.

3,50 m   2,00 m   7-9   ZONE 3

Malus 'Brandywine'
'Brandywine' Crabapple

Amazing bloom! Red buds opening to double pink flowers. Plant in rather rich, cool, well-drained soil. Moderate resistance to most diseases.

Our favorite picks

6,00 m   6,00 m   5   ZONE 4

Malus 'Centurion'
'Centurion' Crabapple

Tree that is covered with flowers in the spring. Dark pink blossoms and fairly disease-resistant purple foliage. Grows in rich, cool, well-drained soil.

7,00 m   5,00 m   5   ZONE 4

Malus 'Dolgo'
'Dolgo' Crabapple

Superb white blooms that give way to big red crabapples. Very disease-resistant, it does well in rich, cool, well-drained soil.

🡡 7,00 m 🡠🡢 6,00 m ❀ 5 ☀ ⚷ ZONE 2 🖐

Malus 'Donald Wyman'
'Donald Wyman' Crabapple

Pinkish white blossoms that turn into tiny red berries that last nearly all winter. Resistant to most diseases. Grow it in rich, cool, well-drained soil.

🡡 6,00 m 🡠🡢 6,00 m ❀ 5 ☀ ZONE 4 🖐

Malus 'Dream Weaver'
'Dream Weaver' Crabapple

If you have a small garden, this crabapple is for you! Columnar variety ideal for enhancing the entrance to the house or a sunny backyard in rich, cool, well-drained soil.

New

🡡 4,00 m 🡠🡢 1,00 m ❀ 5 ☀ ZONE 5 🖐

Malus 'Golden Raindrop'
'Golden Raindrop' Crabapple

Graceful crabapple with deeply cut leaves and tiny yellow crabapples. Plant in rich, cool, well-drained soil. Disease-resistant.

🡡 6,00 m 🡠🡢 5,00 m ❀ 5 ☀ ZONE 4 🖐

Malus 'Prairie Fire'
'Prairie Fire' Crabapple

A good choice under electrical wires because it remains such a reasonable height. Abundant and colourful bloom. Does best in rich, cool, well-drained soil.

6,00 m   6,00 m   5

Malus 'Royalty'
'Royalty' Crabapple

Spring beauty! Purplish foliage, but, above all, dark pink flowers and red crabapples. Decorative tree for rich, cool, well-drained soil. Tolerates heavy soil.

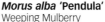

5,00 m   5,00 m   5

Malus sargentii 'Tina'
'Tina' Sargent Crabapple

Remarkable crabapple with spreading branches. Use as an accent plant. Very tolerant to poor, light or heavy, somewhat acid soil. Does best in cool, rich, well-drained soil. Disease-free.

2,00 m   1,50 m   5

Morus alba 'Pendula'
Weeping Mulberry

One of the most beautiful weeping trees. Very easy to grow and resiliant, it does best in soils moderately rich, light, cool, well-drained soil. Edible fruits.

3,00 m   2,00-3,00 m

Physocarpus opulifolius 'Diabolo'
'Diabolo' Ninebark Standard

Incredible top-grafted shrub with very dark purple leaves that highlight the white flowers and red fruits. Very tolerant, it grows in poor, cool, well-drained soil.

2,50-3,00 m   1,25 m   5-6

Populus tremula 'Erecta'
Columnar European Aspen

Very narrow columnar form that bears no fruit. Excellent windbreak. Fast-growing tree in cool and well-drained soils, whether poor or rich, light or heavy, acid or alkaline.

16,00 m   3,00 m

Prunus virginiana 'Schubert'
'Schubert' Chokecherry

Small tree that always does well, no matter what the growing conditions. The soil can be poor or rich, acid or alkaline, dry or moist. Young leaves are green, mature ones are purple.

5,00 m   4,00 m   5

Quercus macrocarpa
Bur Oak

Native hardwood tree of large dimensions that does well in rich, acid or alkaline, cool, well-drained soil.

Our favorite picks

20,00 m   20,00 m

Quercus 'Crimson Spire'
'Crimson Spire' Hybrid Oak

Ideal for small spaces in rich, somewhat acid and cool soil. Columnar growth habit and red fall colour. Something new to discover!

Our favorite picks

![icon] 15,00 m 5,00 m ZONE 5

Quercus rubra
Northern Red Oak

A tree of great value that provides refreshing shade during the heat of summer. Needs rich, acid, cool, well-drained soil. Light or heavy soil.

Our favorite picks

25,00 m 18,00 m ZONE 3

Robinia pseudoacacia 'Twisty Baby'
Corkscrew Black Locust

Deserves to be the focal point of the garden. Small tree with twisting branches that does well in moderately rich, somewhat acid, light, dry soil. Pest-resistant.

3,50 m 3,00 m ZONE 5

Salix 'Prairie Cascade'
'Prairie Cascade' Weeping Willow

Somewhat smaller cousin of the usual weeping willow, with golden yellow twigs. Recommended only for large lots where it prefers moist, light to heavy, poor to rich soil.

15,00 m 10,00 m ZONE 3

Trees 171

Salix purpurea 'Pendula'
Weeping Purpleosier Willow Standard

Fine foliage that gives the small weeping tree a very gracious appearance. Grows equally well in poor or rich, light or heavy, acid or alkaline soil, but always moist.

2,00 m   1,50 m   ☀   ZONE 2

Sorbus aucuparia 'Cardinal Royal'
(syn.: *S. aucuparia* 'Michred')
'Cardinal Royal' European Mountain Ash

An upright tree producing berries that attract birds. Grows in moderately rich, cool, well-drained soil. Beautiful fall colours.

10,00 m   6,00 m   5   ☀   ZONE 3

Syringa meyeri 'Palibin'
Dwarf Korean Lilac Standard

Small rounded lilac, top-grafted to create a small tree. Abundant bloom. Prefers moderately rich, somewhat acid, cool, well-drained soil.

2,00 m   2,00 m   5-6   ☀   ZONE 3

Syringa patula 'Miss Kim'
'Miss Kim' Manchurian Lilac Standard

Lilac blooms that pale as they age. Small grafted tree. Very easy to grow and disease resistant. Likes moderately rich, cool, well-drained soil.

2,00 m   2,00 m   5-6   ☀   ZONE 4

Syringa pekinensis 'China Snow'
(syn.: *S. pekinensis* 'Morton')
'China Snow' Lilac

Coppery bark that is just as attractive as the fragrant creamy white flowers. Undemanding, it grows in friable, well-drained soil. Drought resistant. New and beautiful!

Our favorite picks

⬍ ⬌ ✵ ☀ ❆ ZONE 5 📦
7,50 m 5,50 m 6

Syringa reticulata 'Golden Eclipse'
'Golden Eclipse' Japanese Lilac

This tree, already popular in small gardens, can't help but impress you with its variegated yellow and green foliage. Prefers moderately rich, well-drained soil and tolerates urban conditions. Drought and mildew resistant.

New

⬍ ⬌ ✵ ☀ ❆ ZONE 3 📦
6,00 m 4,00 m 7

Syringa reticulata 'Ivory Silk'
'Ivory Silk' Japanese Lilac

A favourite for city planting, since it tolerates many urban conditions, including pollution, drought, and poor soil. Moderately rich, well-drained soil.

PV

⬍ ⬌ ✵ ☀ ❆ ZONE 2 📦
8,00 m 4,50 m 7

Tilia americana 'Redmond'
'Redmond' American Basswood

Apprecied for its pyramidal habit and the shade it gives the garden. Very fragrant flowers. Prefers rich, cool, well-drained soil.

⬍ ⬌ ✵ ☀ ❆ 🍂 ZONE 3 📦
17,00 m 10,00 m 6

Tilia cordata 'Greenspire'
'Greenspire' Littleleaf Linden

Fast growth and excep-
tional tolerance to
difficult conditions.
Perfectly straight central
trunk and beautiful
shape at maturity.
Prefers rich, somewhat
alkaline, cool, well-
drained soil.

15,00 m   12,00 m   6

Tilia cordata 'Golden Cascade'
'Golden Cascade' Littleleaf Linden

Excellent tree with
a weeping habit and
golden leaves in the fall.
Classy and very hardy.
Cool, well-drained soil.

New

12,00 m   8,00 m

Ulmus 'Accolade' (syn.: U. 'Morton')
'Accolade' Elm

A good replacement for
the American elm, since
it is more resistant to
Dutch elm disease.
Tolerates all soil types
as long as the soil is
cool and well-drained.

18,00 m   12,00 m

Ulmus glabra 'Pendula'
Weeping Elm

A star for the front of the
house! Small weeping
tree that prefers rich,
cool, well-drained soil.
Disease-resistant.

Our favorite picks

6,00 m   10,00 m

The bounty
of the *earth*

To learn about the secrets of the earth, visit
www.fafard.ca

Growing with Confidence

Shrubs

Sambucus canadensis 'Aurea'

Shrubs are indispensable in home landscapes for several reasons.

First, they help link together different groups of plants, both smaller ones and larger ones. They are intermediaries that not only improve the overall structure of the landscape, but also often offer spectacular blooms. From spring through fall, shrubs have varied flowering periods that make them easy to use and their branches full of blooms are even more striking when they are planted in groups.

Not only do they offer colour through their flowers and sometimes through their foliage, but shrubs have silhouettes that suit all sorts of landscapes. Whether they're creeping, upright, rounded or arching, shrubs will always be important players in our landscape designs

◀ *Rhododendron* sp.

Acer ginnala
Amur Maple

⬍ 6,00 m ⬌ 5,00 m ☀ 🌤 ZONE 2 🦅

Tough plant, very hardy and tolerant of difficult living conditions. Not afraid of heavy, poor, dry soil, strong wind or de-icing salts. Prefers moderately rich soil.

Acer palmatum 'Emperor 1'
'Emperor 1' Japanese maple

⬍ 1,50 m ⬌ 1,50 m ☀ 🌤 ZONE 5

One of the hardiest varieties of this beautiful shrub with decorative foliage. Ideal for oriental landscapes. Plant in moderately rich, somewhat acid, cool, well-drained soil.

Alnus glutinosa 'Imperialis'
Cutleaf European Alder

Our favorite picks

⬍ 2,50 m ⬌ 2,50 m ☀ 🌤 🌊 ZONE 4b 🦅 🦋 🐝

Add a note of daintiness to your landscape with this plant's fine foliage. Perfect for Northern gardens. Tolerates all soils, from poor to rich and light to heavy, even very acid. Prefers moist conditions.

Amelanchier canadensis
Shadblow Serviceberry

⬍ 6,00 m ⬌ 3,50 m 5 ❄ ☀ 🌤 ZONE 3 🦅 🦌

Beautiful plant for the urban garden thanks to its spectacular autumn colour and its edible fruits. Birds love it. Grows in poor or rich, light or heavy, somewhat moist soil.

Andromeda polifolia 'Blue Ice'
'Blue Ice' Bog Rosemary

Our *favorite* picks

0,45 m 0,60 m 5 ZONE 2

Acid-loving plant with steel-blue foliage and pretty pink bell-shaped flowers. Needs moist peaty soil. Great companion plant for rhododendrons.

Arctostaphylos uva-ursi
Bearberry

0,10 m 0,70 m 5 ZONE 2

Groundcover shrub with evergreen leaves and very decorative round red berries. Enchanting in a rock garden, ideally in poor, light, acid and rather dry soil.

Aronia melanocarpa 'Autumn Magic'
Black Chokeberry

1,50 m 1,50 m 5-6 ZONE 4

Interesting all year, especially in the autumn, with its black berries and its bright red fall foliage. Does well in poor, acid and somewhat moist soil and tolerates light soils as well as heavy ones.

Berberis thunbergii 'Aurea Nana'
Dwarf Yellow Japanese Barberry

0,70 m 0,70 m 5 ZONE 4

Dense cushion of small bright yellow leaves. Very pretty in the foreground of a flower bed or with other shrubs, in moderately rich, cool, well-drained soil. Tolerates light or heavy soil.

Berberis thunbergii 'Cherry Bomb'
'Cherry Bomb' Japanese Barberry

🌡 0,80 m ↔ 0,80 m ❀ 5 ☀ ☼ ZONE 4 🦌 🚫

Shrub with dark foliage to use in short hedges or as an accent plant. Tolerates light soils as well as heavy ones and prefers moderately rich, cool, well-drained soil.

Berberis thunbergii 'Concorde'
'Concorde' Japanese Barberry

Our favorite picks

🌡 0,40 m ↔ 0,50 m ❀ 5 ☀ ☼ ZONE 4 🦌 🚫

Compact shrub with deep purple foliage becoming scarlet red in fall. Beautiful with roses. Grow in moderately rich, cool, well-drained soil.

Berberis thunbergii 'Rose Glow'
'Pink Glow' Japanese Barberry

Our favorite picks

🌡 1,20 m ↔ 1,00 m ❀ 5 ☀ ☼ ☁ ZONE 4 🦌 🚫

Unique tricolour foliage that adds a great deal of style to the landscape. Very tough. Best planted in moderately rich, cool, well-drained soil.

Berberis thunbergii 'Royal Burgundy'
'Royal Burgundy' Japanese Barberry

🌡 0,60 m ↔ 0,90 m ❀ 5 ☀ ☼ ZONE 4 🦌 🚫

An essential addition to the garden! Magnificent deep purple, very decorative foliage. Can be planted in a wide range of growing conditions, including heavy or light soil.

Betula pendula 'Filigree Lace'
'Filigree Lace' European White Birch

⬍ 1,50 m   ⬌ 1,50 m   ☀ ❉ ᴢᴼᴺᴱ4 🐦

A jewel that should be in the limelight. Semi-weeping shrub with lacy cut foliage that grows well in poor, light, somewhat acid, well-drained soil.

Buddleja davidii 'Adonis Blue'
'Adonis Blue' Butterfly Bush

⬍ 1,20 m   ⬌ 1,00 m   ☀ ❉ ᴢᴼᴺᴱ5 7-9   🐦 🦋 🐛 🦌

Butterfly lovers will want to grow this very floriferous plant. Grows well in moderately rich, rocky, dry soil.

Buddleja davidii 'Peacock'
'Peacock' Butterfly Bush

⬍ 1,20 m   ⬌ 1,00 m   ❉ ☀ ᴢᴼᴺᴱ5 7-9   🐦 🦋 🐛 🦌

The same beautiful blooms that attract butterflies in a format more interesting for smaller space gardens. Plant in moderately rich, somewhat dry soil.

Buddleja davidii 'Purple Emperor'
'Purple Emperor' Butterfly Bush

⬍ 1,50 m   ⬌ 1,20 m   ❉ ☀ ᴢᴼᴺᴱ5 7-9   🐦 🦋 🐛 🦌

Constant blooms that attract butterflies. More compact format that tolerates rocky soil. Grows in moderately rich, dry soil.

Buxus microphylla 'Green Velvet'
'Green Velvet' Japanese Boxwood

⌐⌐ 0,60 m ⌐⌐ 0,60 m ☀ ❄ 🌊 ZONE 5 🦌

Ideal for short formal hedges. Shrub with evergreen foliage that should be planted in light, moderately rich, cool, well-drained soil.

Cephalanthus occidentalis
Common Buttonbush

Our favorite picks

⌐⌐ 2,00 m ⌐⌐ 3,00 m ☀ 🌊 ZONE 4 🦋 7-8

Native plant bearing perfectly round, fragrant blooms. Loves the edge of ponds in moist, slightly acid soil. Grows well in poor or rich, light or heavy soil.

Calluna vulgaris 'Marleen'
'Marleen' Common Heather

⌐⌐ 0,25 m ⌐⌐ 0,45 m 9-10 ❄ ☀ 🌊 ZONE 5 🦌

Small cushion-like shrub blooming very late and preferring acid soil. Plant in small clumps as an edging plant in poor, acid, light, well-draining, cool soil. Remains in bloom until the following spring.

Clethra alnifolia 'Ruby Spice'
'Ruby Spice' Summersweet

⌐⌐ 1,00 m ⌐⌐ 1,00 m ☀ 🌊 ZONE 4 🦋 7-8

Clear pink blooms that are well worth discovering. This small shrub, little-known yet very reliable, grows well in slightly moist, acid, rich soil.

Cornus alba 'Ivory Halo'
'Ivory Halo' Tartarian Dogwood

🔼 1,50 m   ↔ 1,50 m   ❄ 6   ☀   ☼   ZONE 3   🐾

Variegated foliage on a dense, luxuriant shrub. It's used as much as a foundation plant as an accent plant. Has no trouble tolerating poor, light or heavy, acid or alkaline, slightly moist soil.

Cornus pumila
Dwarf Dogwood

🔼 1,20 m   ↔ 1,50 m   ❄ 6   ☀   ☼   ZONE 4   🐾

The perfect subject for smaller lots. New shoots are red on a slightly spreading shrub. Tolerates different growing conditions including poor, heavy, acid or slightly moist soil.

Cornus stolonifera 'Flaviramea'
Yellowbark Red-Osier Dogwood

🔼 1,50 m   ↔ 2,00 m   ❄ 6   ☀   ☼   ☁   ZONE 3   🌱   🐾

Still highly appreciated for its yellow stems, decorative in winter. Doesn't need much care. Grow in beds in rich, somewhat moist, slightly acid soil.

Corylus avellana 'Red Majestic'
'Red Majestic' Contorted Filbert

🔼 1,50 m   ↔ 1,50 m   ❄ 5   ☀   ☼   ☁   ZONE 5   🌱

Just as twisted as the old contorted filbert, but with purple leaves, catkins, and nuts. Unique plant for a starring role. Does best in a spot protected from the wind in rich, cool, well-drained soil.

Cotinus coggygria 'Golden Spirit'
'Golden Spirit' Smoketree

2,00 m 2,00 m 7-8 ZONE 5

Rounded golden yellow leaves in summer that turn reddish orange in the fall. Enhances the appearance of neighbouring plants when grown in flower beds. Light, dry soil.

Cotinus coggygria 'Royal Purple'
'Royal Purple' Smoketree

2,50 m 2,00 m 7-8 ZONE 4

Tall background shrub with frothy flowers. The best known of the dark purple smoketrees. For moderately rich, light, dry soil.

Cotinus coggygria 'Young Lady'
'Young Lady' Smoketree

New

1,00 m 1,20 m 7-8 ZONE 5

New variety of this unique shrub that flowers abundantly on a smaller, younger plant. Grows in moderately rich, light, somewhat acid, dry soil.

Cotoneaster adpressus var. praecox
Creeping Cotoneaster

1.00 M 1.50 M ZONE 5

An excellent groundcover for growing at the base of trees and shrubs. Covered with round scarlet berries in late summer. Prefers light, somewhat acid, dry soil.

Daphne cneorum
Rose Daphne

0.30 m   0.70 m   5   ZONE 4

For rock gardens or acid-soil gardens. Charming bluish evergreen foliage with exquisite blooms. Likes rocky, moderately rich, cool, well-drained soil.

Daphne mezereum
Mezereon

Our favorite picks

0.80 m   0.050 m   5   ZONE 3

Small shrub with upright stems and deciduous foliage. Good companion to rhododendrons in acid, rich, cool, well-drained soil. Tolerates both heavy and light soil.

Elaeagnus angustifolia
Russian Olive

8,00 m   8,00 m   5   ZONE 2

Tough pollution-resistant plant with grey foliage. Needs light, somewhat alkaline, moderately rich, dry soil.

Erica carnea 'Springwood White'
'Springwood White' Winter Heath

0,20 m   0,45 m   4   ZONE 5

Groundcover shrub that loves acid soil and blooms at snowmelt. Perfect as a companion to rhododendrons in poor, peaty, cool soil.

Euonymus alatus 'Chicago Fire'
'Chicago Fire' Burning Bush

Our favorite picks

⬆ 2,50 m   ↔ 2,00 m   ☀ ☼ ⬜ZONE 4 ✋

The most beautiful fall colour of all is the fire engine red of this big shrub. It can be used as a screen or a specimen plant. Does well everywhere as long as the soil remains cool and well-drained.

Euonymus alatus 'Compactus'
Dwarf Burning Bush

PV

⬆ 1,50-1,80 m   ↔ 1,20 m   ☀ ☼ ⬜ZONE 4 ✋

Compact form of this beautiful shrub famous for its spectacular fall colour. Grows well in rich or poor, light or heavy, acid or alkaline soil. Perfect for smaller yards.

Euonymus fortunei 'Blondy'
'Blondy' Wintercreeper

New

⬆ 0,45 m   ↔ 1,00 m   ☼ ⬜ ⬜ZONE 5

An excellent subject for mixed perennial borders to which it brings colour and contrast. Happy in rich, cool, well-drained soil.

Euonymus fortunei 'Emerald Gaiety'
'Emerald Gaiety' Wintercreeper

⬆ 1,20 m   ↔ 2,00 m   ☀ ☼ ⬜ ⬜ZONE 5

Always popular! Small shrub with decorative evergreen leaves. Perfectly suited to rock gardens or edges of shrub borders. Plant in rich, cool, well-drained soil.

Euonymus fortunei 'Emerald'n Gold'
'Emerald'n Gold' Wintercreeper

1,20 m   2,00 m

ZONE 5

Striking evergreen foliage on a small shrub that does well in rich, cool, well-drained soil. For a beautiful contrast, grow with blue-flowered plants.

Forsythia 'Marée d'Or' (syn.: *F.* 'Courtasol')
'Marée d'Or' Forsythia

0,75 m   1,50 m   5

ZONE 4

Spreading shrub completely covered with golden yellow flowers before the leaves appear in spring. Tolerates many growing conditions including poor, dry, heavy or light soils as well as shade.

Forsythia 'Northern Gold'
'Northern Gold' Forsythia

2,00 m   1,50 m   5

ZONE 4

Tall shrub used as a background plant in flower beds. Blooms very early, before the leaves come out. Very tolerant, it prefers moderately rich, cool, well-drained soil.

Gaultheria procumbens
Wintergreen

0,10 m   0,60 m   5

ZONE 2

Groundcover with shiny evergreen foliage, able to live under conifers. Foliage has a minty flavour. Plant in poor, acid, cool, well-drained soil.

Genista pilosa 'Vancouver Gold'
'Vancouver Gold' Silky Bloom

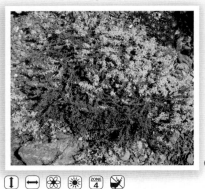

☐ 0,25 ☐ 0,80 ☐ 5-6 ☐ ☐ ZONE 4 ☐

Exceptional choice in beds or on slopes. Decorative green stems in winter. Happy in poor, light, dry soil.

Halimodendron halodendron
Common Salttree

☐ 2,50 m ☐ 2,00 m ☐ 5-6 ☐ ☐ ZONE 3

Highly resistant to extreme conditions, like salt air near the ocean, violent winds, and dry soil. Prefers moderately rich, light soil.

Hamamelis virginiana
Common Witchhazel

☐ 2,00 m ☐ 2,00 m ☐ 9 ☐ ☐ ☐ ZONE 4 ☐ ☐

Good screening plant blooming very late in the fall, with golden fall foliage. Likes rich, somewhat acid, cool, well-drained soil. Pest-free native plant.

Hippophae rhamnoides
Common Seabuckthorn

☐ 3,00 m ☐ 3,00 m ☐ ☐ ☐ ZONE 4 ☐

A must in difficult conditions. Grey leaves and decorative orange berries. Plant in groups, ideally in rich, light, somewhat alkaline, dry soil. Tends to produce suckers.

Hydrangea arborescens 'Annabelle'
'Annabelle' Smooth Hydrangea

1,20 m   1,50 m   7-9   ZONE 3

A classic, renowned for its abundant bloom. Grows wonderfully with no care at all. Prefers rich, cool soil, but tolerates far from perfect conditions.

Hydrangea arborescens 'White Dome'
'White Dome' Smooth Hydrangea

Our favorite picks

1,20 m   1,20 m   7-9   ZONE 3

Generous inflorescence made up of sterile and fertile flowers on solid stems. Plant in beds in rich, somewhat acid, cool, well-drained soil. Easy to grow.

Hydrangea macrophylla 'Endless Summer'
'Endless Summer' Mophead Hydrangea

Our favorite picks

1,00 m   1,00 m   6-9   ZONE 4

Variety that blooms on the current year's wood, which guarantees even more spectacular flowers. Needs acid, rich, peaty and slightly moist soil.

Hydrangea macrophylla 'Shamrock'
'Shamrock' Mophead Hydrangea

1,00 m   1,00 m   7-8   ZONE 5

Superb sterile double flowers of great beauty. Likes acid, rich, peaty and slightly moist soil. Protect in winter to guarantee bloom.

Hydrangea macrophylla 'Pia'
'Pia' Mophead Hydrangea

🔼 0,80 m ↔ 0,80 m ❋ 7-8 ☀ ☼ 🌱 ⬛ ZONE 5

Large, vividly coloured flowers on compact plants. Plant in border in a protected spot, in acid, slightly moist soil.

Hydrangea paniculata 'Grandiflora'
Peegee Hydrangea

🔼 2,00 m ↔ 2,00 m ❋ 7-9 ☀ ☼ ZONE 3

One of the most spectacular blooms of the end of summer. Easy to grow and pest-free. Plant in hedges or small groups in rich, slightly moist soil.

Hydrangea paniculata 'Kyushu'
'Kyushu' Panicle Hydrangea

🔼 2,00 m ↔ 1,50 m ❋ 7-9 ☀ ☼ ZONE 3

Very elegant variety, with upright stems and a long period of bloom. Reliable and easy to grow. Plant it in small groups or as a specimen plant in rich, slightly moist soil.

Hydrangea paniculata 'Limelight'
'Limelight' Panicle Hydrangea

Our favorite picks

🔼 2,00 m ↔ 2,00 m ❋ 7-8 ☀ ☼ ZONE 4

White blooms with a lime green tinge early in the season, then becoming creamy white. Tough and floriferous plant that grows easily in different soils. Prefers cool, slightly moist soil.

Hydrangea paniculata 'Little Lamb'
'Little Lamb' Panicle Hydrangea

Our favorite picks

🔼 2,00 m　◀▶ 2,00 m　❀ 7-8　☀　❄　ZONE 4

Unique due the tiny petals of its flowers. Easy to integrate into any landscape and especially appreciates the company of shrubs and perennials in cool and somewhat moist soil.

Hydrangea paniculata 'Mega Pearl'
'Mega Pearl' Panicle Hydrangea

🔼 2,50 m　◀▶ 1,80 m　❀ 7-8　☀　❄　ZONE 3

Enormous panicles of white flowers turning deep pink in the fall. Impressive! Grow in rich, slightly moist soil.

Hydrangea paniculata 'Pink Diamond'
'Pink Diamond' Panicle Hydrangea

Our favorite picks

🔼 2,00 m　◀▶ 2,00 m　❀ 7-9　☀　❄　ZONE 3

Shrub of great value in the garden for its late summer and fall bloom. Reliable, very hardy and requiring little care, it is best planted in rich and somewhat moist soil.

Hydrangea paniculata 'Pinky Winky'
'Pinky Winky' Panicle Hydrangea

New

🔼 2,00 m　◀▶ 2,00 m　❀ 7-9　☀　❄　ZONE 4

Magnificent gradation of colours on the same inflorescence. Now imagine dozens of these flowers! Easy to grow, pest- and disease-free, this hydrangea prefers rich, slightly moist soil.

Hydrangea paniculata 'Quick Fire'
'Quick Fire' Panicle Hydrangea

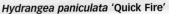

🌱 2,00 m ↔ 2,00 m ❄ 6-9 ☀ 🌤 ZONE 3

Earlier to bloom than the other panicle hydrangeas. The flowers take on a very attractive dark pink coloration in fall. Tough, it prefers rich, slightly moist soil.

Hydrangea paniculata 'Unique'
'Unique' Panicle Hydrangea

PV

🌱 2,00 m ↔ 1,50 m ❄ 8-10 ☀ 🌤 ZONE 3

No garden should go without it! Original and reliable flowers on a very hardy, tough plant. Plant in rich, slightly moist soil in small groups or as a specimen plant.

Hydrangea serrata 'Arctic Blue'
'Arctic Blue' Mountain Hydrangea

🌱 1,00 m ↔ 0,70 m ❄ 7-8 ☀ 🌤 ZONE 4 🐦

Promising! This hydrangea has flowers like those of the mophead hydrangeas, but much hardier. Excellent substitute for use in rich, somewhat acid, cool soil.

Ilex verticillata 'Berry Heavy'
'Berry Heavy' Winterberry

🌱 2,00 m ↔ 2,00 m ☀ ZONE 4 🐦

Tons of scarlet red berries! This deciduous holly prefers moist, rich and somewhat acid soil. Attracts birds to the garden.

Itea virginica 'Sprich' (syn.: *I. virginica* 'Little Henry')
'Sprich' Virginia Sweetspire

0,80 m	1,20 m	6			ZONE 5	

Little known plant that does well in rather moist, rich, slightly acid soil. Startling blooms and beautiful fall colours.

Magnolia loebneri 'Merrill'
'Merrill' Magnolia

Our favorite picks

6,00 m	7,00 m	5			ZONE 4	

Surprisingly hardy! This shrub with spectacular early flowers does well in rich, somewhat acid, cool, well-drained soil. Plant so it is sheltered from the wind for better blooms.

Magnolia soulangiana
Saucer Magnolia

5,00 m	4,00 m	5			ZONE 5	

Impressive flowers appear very early in the spring. Plant so it is sheltered from the wind in moderately rich, slightly acid, cool, well-drained soil. Magnificent!

Malus 'Coccinella' (syn. M. 'Courtarou')
'Coccinella' Crabapple

5,00 m	3,00 m	5			ZONE 3	

Tiny crabapple with abundant bloom. Very disease-resistant! Grows well in rich, cool, well-drained soil. Tolerates heavy soil.

Myrica gale
Sweet Gale

⬆ 1,20 m ↔ 2,00 m ❋ ☀ ☼ ᴢᴏɴᴇ 2 ⚒ 🝤 ⬙

For the edge of ponds, water gardens and streams since it likes moist, peaty, acid soil. Beautiful bluish leaves smelling of camphor.

Philadelphus 'Snowbelle'
'Snowbelle' Mockorange

⬆ 1,20 m ↔ 1,00 m 6 ❋ ☀ ☼ ᴢᴏɴᴇ 4 🦋 🝤 ⬙

Masses of double highly fragrant flowers on an easy-to-grow shrub. Use in shrub borders in rich, cool, well-drained soil.

Physocarpus opulifolius 'Coppertina'
'Coppertina' Ninebark

New

⬆ 2,00 m ↔ 1,50 m 5-6 ❋ ☀ ☼ ᴢᴏɴᴇ 3 ⚒

Unique foliage. New shrub with foliage tinged red, bronze, and copper. Plant behind perennials or in small groups in rather poor, cool, well-drained soil.

Physocarpus opulifolius 'Dart's Gold'
'Dart's Gold' Ninebark

⬆ 1,50 m ↔ 1,50 m 5-6 ❋ ☀ ☼ ᴢᴏɴᴇ 2 ⚒

Beautifully coloured leaves make it useful in various spots in the garden. Plant in poor, cool, well-drained soil. A survivor!

Physocarpus opulifolius 'Diabolo'
'Diabolo' Ninebark

Our favorite picks

2,00 m 1,50 m 5-6 ZONE 2

Pretty all year and and easy to grow. Spectacular shrub with very dark leaves that bring out the white flowers and then the brilliant red berries. Poor, cool, well-drained soil.

Physocarpus opulifolius 'Summer Wine'
'Summer Wine' Ninebark

Our favorite picks

1,50 m 1,50 m 6 ZONE 2

A contrasting look in a very easy-to-grow shrub. Tough and very hardy, it can be used in poor, cool, well-drained soil.

Potentilla fruticosa 'Abbotswood'
'Abbotswood' Shrubby Cinquefoil

0,80 m 1,50 m 6-9 ZONE 2

Heat and drought-resistant, this cinquefoil really stands out from the crowd. This bushy cultivar with pure white flowers blooms non-stop. Moderately rich, light or heavy, cool, well-drained soil.

Potentilla fruticosa 'Goldfinger'
'Goldfinger' Shrubby Cinquefoil

1,00 m 1,00 m 6-9 ZONE 2

A classic appreciated for its beautiful appearance even in difficult growing conditions. Use to form a low hedge or plant in a shrub border.

Potentilla fruticosa 'Goldstar'
'Goldstar' Shrubby CInquefoil

0,80 m   1,20 m   6-9

Spreading shrub appreciated for its tolerance to heat and to poor, light or heavy soil. Good groundcover with very large flowers. Prefers moderately rich, cool, well-drained soil.

Potentilla fruticosa 'Mango Tango'
'Mango Tango' Shrubby CInquefoil

0,60 m   0,60 m   6-9

A mix of deep yellow and orange flowers on the same plant. Unique colour for a cinquefoil, which doesn't stop it from being just as tough as its cousins.

Ptelea trifoliata 'Aurea'
Golden Hoptree

3,00 m   2,50 m   6   4

A spreading shrub that does well in dry conditions, whether the soil is poor or rich, light or heavy. Interesting trifoliate golden leaves. Flattened seeds much like those of elms.

Rhamnus frangula 'Fine Line'
'Fine Line' Fernleaf Buckthorn

Our favorite picks

2,00 m   0,75 m   3

Very hardy and both tough and delicate at the same time. A refined look for gardens in very cold climates. Upright shrub that prefers heavy, very acid, cool, well-drained soil. Noninvasive.

Rhododendron 'Elviira'
'Elviira' Finnish Hybrid Rhododendron

0,75 m	0,75 m	6			ZONE 4	

Superb brilliant red blooms on hardy plants. As with all rhododendrons, plant in a spot protected from the wind. Prefers very acid, cool, well-drained soil.

Rhododendron 'Golden Lights'
'Golden Lights' Azalea

PV

1,50 m	1,20 m	6			ZONE 4	

One of the hardier azaleas, it bears abundant tangerine orange blossoms. Pretty with golden-leaved hostas. Needs acid, cool, well-drained soil.

Rhododendron 'Haaga'
'Haaga' Finnish Hybrid Rhododendron

Our favorite picks

1,00 m	1,00 m	6			ZONE 4	

Interesting in shady beds with ferns. Great masses of bright pink flowers. Plant in acid, cool, well-drained soil.

Rhododendron 'Hellikki'
'Hellikki' Finnish Hybrid Rhododendron

Our favorite picks

1,00 m	1,50 m	6			ZONE 4	

Spectacular bloom for the shade garden. Finnish hybrid with dark evergreen leaves. Plant so it is sheltered from the wind, in acid, cool, well-drained soil.

Rhododendron 'Mandarin Lights'
'Mandarin Lights' Azalea

Our favorite picks

1.20 m   1,20 m   6

Very colourful spring blooms. Grow with other rhododendrons and azaleas in acid, peaty, cool, well-drained soil.

Rhododendron 'Mikkeli'
'Mikkeli' Finnish Hybrid Rhododendron

Our favorite picks

0,90 m   1,00 m   6

Evergreen shrub whose remarkable white blooms have a slightly pinkish tinge. Loves acid, cool, well-drained soil where it can grow in the company of shade plants.

Rhododendron 'Nova Zembla'
'Nova Zembla' Rhododendron

1,00 m   1,00 m   6

Superb purplish red blooms appear in great numbers on this small shrub with big evergreen leaves. Plant with heucheras in acid, cool, well-drained soil.

Rhododendron 'Peter Tigerstedt'
'Peter Tigerstedt' Finnish Hybrid Rhododendron

1,80 m   1,20 m   6

A large, especially hardy shrub with evergreen leaves and white blooms spotted mauve. Plant so it is sheltered from the wind in cool, well-drained and acid soil.

Rhododendron 'PJM'
'PJM' Rhododendron

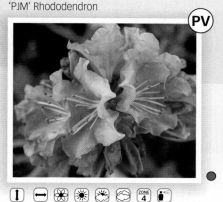

1,75 m 1,50 m 5

A springtime treasure with blooms so abundant they completely cover the foliage. Quite hardy, it can be planted in acid, cool and well-drained soil, in a spot protected from winter winds.

Rhododendron 'Ramapo'
'Ramapo' Rhododendron

0,60 m 0,75 m 5

Small rounded shrub that likes growing with dwarf conifers. Plant in bed or in a rock garden, in acid, cool, well-drained soil.

Rhododendron 'Rosy Lights'
'Rosy Lights' Azalea

1,50 m 1,25 m 6

Unbeatable springtime beauty! Spectacular, fragrant bloom that will draw everyone's attention. Plant in cool, rich, acid and well-drained soil.

Rhus typhina 'Laciniata'
Cutleaf Staghorn Sumac

3,00 m 2,00 m

You'll be surprised and pleased by its finely cut leaves. This exotic-looking plant is perfectly hardy and will grow in poor, rocky, somewhat acid, dry soil.

Rhus typhina 'Tiger Eyes'
Golden Staghorn Sumac

3,00 m   2,00 m

Superb finely cut foliage which is golden yellow all summer, yet turns bright red in the fall. Easy-to-grow plant that does well in poor, somewhat acid, dry soil.

Salix integra 'Flamingo'
'Flamingo' Japanese Willow

1,00 m   1,50 m

New growth is tinted bright pink to red and holds its colour all summer. A great screening plant for various soils, including poor, heavy, acid or moist soil.

Salix integra 'Hakuro Nishiki'
Japanese Dappled Willow

1,80 m   1,50 m

Superb shrub with delicate stems and leaves spotted cream and pink. For difficult spots like poor, light or heavy, acid or alkaline, moist soil.

Salix purpurea 'Nana'
Purpleosier Willow

1,50 m   1,50 m

Remarkably graceful greyish foliage. Free-growing shrub for in beds or as a specimen plant in poor to rich, light to heavy, acid to alkaline, moist soil.

Salix matsudana 'Tortuosa'
Corkscrew Willow

8,00 m   4,50 m

Interesting because of its twisting branches that are very popular in floral arrangements. Needs light and slightly moist soil and a spot protected from strong winds.

Sambucus canadensis 'Aurea'
Golden American Elder

3,00 m   2,00 m   6-7

A large shrub with interesting decorative foliage that can dress up the area around the house. Plant in cool, moderately rich, somewhat acid and rather moist soil.

Sambucus nigra 'Black Lace' (syn.: S. nigra 'Eva')
'Black Lace' Elder

2,50 m   2,00 m   6-7

It looks like a Japanese maple with dark foliage! Magnificent finely cut leaves are nearly black. An accent plant that will grow in many types of soil.

Sambucus nigra 'Laciniata'
Cutleaf Black Elder

1,50 m   1,50 m   6-7

Finely cut leaves that give the garden a graceful appearance. Magnificent near a water garden or combined with large-leaved shrubs. Grows in all soil types except dry.

Sambucus racemosa 'Sutherland Gold'
'Sutherland Gold' Red Elder

3,00 m 3,00 m 6-7

Wow! Superb deeply cut leaves in bright golden yellow. Plant of great interest in every way: very hardy, pest-free, and adapted to rich, cool, well-drained soil.

Sorbaria sorbifolia 'Appleberry'
'Appleberry' Sorbaria

1,80 m 1,75 m 6-7

More docile than the usual sorbaria, it forms attractive masses of foliage without becoming invasive. Grows even in rocky, poor or dry soil, but prefers cool conditions.

Sorbaria sorbifolia
Sorbaria

1,80 m 2,00 m 6-7

Vigorous plant that forms pretty masses of foliage, even under difficult growing conditions like rocky, poor or dry soil. Prefers rich and somewhat moist soil.

Sorbaria sorbifolia 'Sem'
'Sem' Sorbaria

1,00 m 1,00 m 6-7

Very interesting foliage in the spring when new growth is bronze-coloured. It becomes green in summer. Compact variety that adapts to all possible growing conditions. This variety is less invasive than the species.

Spiraea cinerea 'Grefsheim'
Elf's Home Spirea

🌡 ↔ ✼ ☀ ZONE 4 🦋 🐦

1,50m 1,50m 5

Graceful branches bearing pure white flowers in early spring. Spectacular both as a hedge plant and as a specimen plant. Undemanding, it likes moderately rich, cool, well-drained soil.

Spiraea japonica 'Anthony Waterer'
'Anthony Waterer' Japanese Spirea

🌡 ↔ ✼ ☀ ✼ ZONE 2 🦋 🐦

0,90 m 0,90 m 7-9

Ideal plant for the novice gardener. Grows and flowers with almost no care! Does just as well in heavy as light soil, but prefers rich, cool, well-drained soil.

Spiraea fritschiana 'Wilma'
(syn.: *S. fritschiana* 'Pink Parasols')
Pink Parasols Spirea

(PV)

🌡 ↔ ✼ ☀ ✼ ZONE 4 🦋 🐦

1,00 m 1,20 m 6

Beautiful frothy pink flower clusters. Good border plant and easy to grow, it does well in poor or rich, light or heavy, cool, well-drained soil.

Spiraea japonica 'Dakota Goldcharm'
(syn.: *S. japonica* 'Mertyann')
'Dakota Goldcharm' Japanese Spirea

🌡 ↔ ✼ ☀ ✼ ZONE 4 🦋 🐦

0,45 m 0,60 m 7-8

Perfect little ball of golden foliage with pink flowers. Just what you need for the rock garden or as an edging plant in rich, cool, well-drained soil. Pest-free and always beautiful.

Spiraea japonica 'Flaming Mound'
'Flaming Mound' Japanese Spirea

PV

0,60 m 0,60 m 7-9

A rounded shrub with decorative leaves. New sprouts are at first reddish, then become pale green. Beautiful fall colours. Rich, cool, well-drained soil.

Spiraea japonica 'Gold Mound'
'Gold Mound' Japanese Spirea

0,70 m 0,80 m 7-9

Big seller. Popular variety with golden foliage renowned for its toughness. Ideal beginner plant. Tolerates heavy or light soil, but prefers rich, cool, well-drained soil.

Spiraea japonica 'Little Princess'
'Little Princess' Japanese Spirea

0,60 m 0,60 m 7-9

Very small but also very cute. Use it as a low hedge along paths or in small gardens in rich, cool, well-drained soil. Tolerates heavy soil.

Spiraea japonica 'Magic Carpet'
'Magic Carpet' Japanese Spirea

Our favorite picks

0,40 m 0,60 m 7-8

Tiny rounded shrub that needs little pruning. Interesting for smaller yards, rock gardens or small formal hedges. Suitable for rich, cool, well-drained soil.

Spiraea japonica 'Shirobana'
'Shirobana' Japanese Spirea

0,80 m   0,80 m   7-9

Each inflorescence has both white and dark pink flowers, which creates an interesting effect. Good foundation plant for rich, cool moist soils. Tolerates heavy soil.

Spiraea nipponica 'Snowmound'
Snowmound Spirea

1,20 m   0,80 m   6

Covered with white flowers in the spring. Easy to grow and can be used both as a specimen plant or integrated into a shrub border in rich, cool, well-drained soil.

Spiraea x vanhouttei
Vanhoutte Spirea

2,00 m   1,75 m   6

Abundant, magical bloom in spring gave it its lovely nickname "bridal wreath spirea". Very tolerant, it prefers rich soil whether heavy or light, dry or very moist.

Stephanandra incisa 'Crispa'
Dwarf Cutleaf Stephanandra

Our favorite picks

0,50 m   1,50 m   6

Creeping plant with arching branches, perfect for replacing creeping junipers. Adapted to difficult conditions, it grows best in rich, somewhat acid, cool, well-drained soil. Easy!

Shrubs 205

Symphoricarpos albus
Snowberry

⬍ ⬌ ❅ ☀ ⛅ 〜 ZONE 2 🐾 🦌

1,50 m 1,50 m 6

One of the rare shrubs that grows in shade in poor soil. Native plant with round white berries that prefers moderately rich, light, cool, well-drained soil.

Symphoricarpos 'Amethyst'
'Amethyst' Coralberry

⬍ ⬌ ❅ ☀ ⛅ 〜 ZONE 3 🐾 🦌

1,25 m 1,25 m 6

Surprising rounded pinkish purple berries on a shrub adapted to many growing conditions. Needs little care. Grows best in light, cool, well-drained soil.

Syringa hyacinthiflora 'Pocahontas'
'Pocahontas' Early Lilac

Our favorite picks

⬍ ⬌ ❅ ☀ ⛅ ZONE 3 🦋 ▣ 🦌

3,00 m 2,50 m 5-6

Early flowers with a very intense fragrance! Let a spring-blooming clematis climb on it for a beautiful effect. Plant in moderately rich, cool, well-drained soil.

Syringa 'Josée'
'Josée' Lilac

⬍ ⬌ ❅ ☀ ZONE 4 🦋 ▣ 🦌

1,20 m 1,20 m 6-9

Dwarf lilac that can flower more than once during the summer if its faded flowers are removed. Undemanding, this lilac requires moderately rich, cool, well-drained soil.

Syringa meyeri 'Palibin'
Dwarf Korean Lilac

1,00 m   0,80 m   6

Small rounded shrub that is covered in pink flowers in spring. Easy to grow if planted in moderately rich, somewhat acid, cool, well-drained soil.

Syringa patula 'Miss Kim'
'Miss Kim' Manchurian Lilac

1,50 m   2,00 m   6

Big lilac-coloured inflorescences on a small rounded shrub. Beautiful accent plant in moderately rich, cool, well-drained soil. Disease-resistant.

Syringa prestoniae 'Donald Wyman'
'Donald Wyman' Preston Lilac

2,50 m   2,00m   6

Beautiful deep purple flowers on a shrub that likes moderately rich, somewhat acid, cool, well-drained soil. Blooms later than the common lilac.

Syringa vulgaris 'Charles Joly'
'Charles Joly' Common Lilac

3,00 m   2,50 m   6

One of the prettiest cultivars, it has very deeply coloured double purple flowers with an intense fragrance. Adapts to many soils, but prefers moderately rich, cool, well-drained soil.

Syringa vulgaris 'Mme Lemoine'
'Mme Lemoine' Common Lilac

⬆ ⬌ ❄ ☀ ❅ [ZONE 3] Ⓜ 📷 🐾

3,00 m   3,00 m   6

Magnificent double white flowers that give off a powerful fragrance. Does well in moderately rich, cool and well-drained soil, but tolerates other conditions.

Tamarix ramosissima 'Pink Cascade'
'Pink Cascades' Tamarisk

⬆ ⬌ ❄ ☀ ❅ [ZONE 4]

2,00 m   1,80 m   7-8

Novel plant on all levels with its incredibly fine foliage and light, airy flowers. Grows well in rocky, somewhat alkaline, dry soil. Tolerates poor soil.

Syringa vulgaris 'Wedgewood Blue'
'Wedgewood Blue' Common Lilac

⬆ ⬌ ❄ ☀ ❅ [ZONE 3] Ⓜ 📷 🐾

4,00 m   3,00 m   6

Pink flower buds open into superb sky blue flowers, one of the purest blues of all the lilacs. Plant in moderately rich, cool, well-drained soil.

Viburnum dentatum 'Blue Muffin'
(syn.: *V. dentatum* 'Christom')
'Blue Muffin' Arrowwood Viburnum

Our favorite picks

⬆ ⬌ ❄ ☀ ❅ ◠ [ZONE 3] 🌱 Ⓜ 🐾

2,00 m   1,50 m   6

New and exciting! The perfect size for home gardens. Covered with hundreds of blue berries in late summer. Likes heavy and slightly moist soil. Tolerates acid or alkaline conditions.

Viburnum dilatatum 'Henneke'
(syn.: *V. dilatatum* 'Cardinal Candy')
'Cardinal Cardy' Linden Viburnum

2,00m 2,00m 5

Interesting for the winter garden. Produces dense clusters of tiny cardinal red berries that last until winter. Rich, heavy and somewhat moist soil.

Viburnum lantana 'Mohican'
'Mohican' Wayfaring Tree Viburnum

Our favorite picks

2,00 m 2,50 m 5

Agréable sur plusieurs saisons: floraison blanche au printemps et fruits décoratifs en été et en automne. Se plaît dans un sol lourd, un peu acide et légèrement humide.

Viburnum trilobum 'Compactum'
Dwarf Highbush Cranberry

1,50 m 1,50 m 6

Miniature version of the native shrub loved by birds. Red berries that last through much of the winter and beautiful fall colours. Likes rich, heavy, somewhat acid, slightly moist soil.

Weigela 'Carnaval'
'Carnaval' Weigela

PV

1,50 m 1,50 m 6-7

Beautiful trumpet-shaped flowers in various shades of pink. Attracts hummingbirds. Grows well in rich, cool and well-drained soil, but tolerates other growing conditions.

Weigela florida 'French Lace'
(syn.: *W. florida* 'Brigela')
'French Lace' Weigela

(PV)

⬆ ↔ ❄ ☀ 🌤 ZONE 4 🐦

1,20 m 1,20 m 7-8

Very classy. Leaves delicately bordered in lime green. Magnificent flowers! Undemanding and pest-free plant, it grows well in rich, cool, well-drained soil.

Weigela 'Minuet'
'Minuet' Weigela

⬆ ↔ ❄ ☀ 🌤 ZONE 3 🐦 🪴

0,60 m 0,60 m 6-7

A small weigela that is very pretty in groups with its foliage lightly tinted purple. Appreciated by hummingbirds, this shrub grows in rich, cool, well-drained soil.

Weigela florida 'Midnight Wine'
(syn.: *W. florida* 'Elvera')
'Midnight Wine' Weigela

⬆ ↔ ❄ ☀ 🌤 ZONE 4 🐦

0,60 m 0,60 m 6-7

Just as spectacular as 'Wine & Roses' but in a miniature version. This small shrub is perfect for perennial or shrub borders where it thrives in rich, cool soil.

Weigela florida 'My Monet'
'My Monet' Weigela

New

⬆ ↔ ❄ ☀ 🌤 ZONE 5

30-45 m 30-45 m 6-7

Free the artist deep within thanks to this shrub with tricolour leaves which is beautiful all year. In mass plantings or mixed with perennials, it is always attractive. Prefers rich, cool, well-drained soil.

Weigela 'Red Prince'
'Red Prince' Weigela

1,50 m   1,20 m   7-8

A sight to behold entirely covered with flowers! A large shrub remarkable as much for its flowers as for its graceful shape. It needs rich, cool, well-drained soil.

Weigela florida 'Wine & Roses'
(syn.: *W. florida* 'Alexandra')
'Wine & Roses' Weigela

0,80 m   1,20 m   7-8

So romantic! Very deep purple foliage and trumpet-shaped flowers on a low-growing shrub that does best in rich, cool, well-drained soil. A must for any garden!

Weigela 'Vampire'
'Vampire' Weigela

1,00 m   1,00 m   6

Imagine red velvety flowers against such foliage! A compact weigela hardier than most with deep purple leaves. It prefers rich, cool, well-drained soil. Hybrid developed in Quebec.

Yucca filamentosa
Adam's Needle

   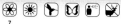

1,00 m   1,00 m   7

Huge fragrant flower spike borne well above the rosette of spiny foliage. Does best in poor, rocky, dry soil. Likes the heat.

Hedges

A hedge of flowering shrubs is always a treat for the eye.

Its linear effect gives force to this group of shrubs chosen for their resistance and density. Besides organizing space and establishing property lines, hedges participate in creating a milder micro-climate by slowing the wind and helping snow to accumulate, so important in the survival of plants in our climate. Hedges become screens when the plants chosen gain enough height and density to hide undesirable views or to reduce ambient sounds. Nearly any shrub can become a hedge, even the shortest ones; they can follow a path, half close a patio or terrace, define a vegetable bed, etc. Certain hedge plants are sold bare-root in the spring,, leading to reduced costs and easier planting. Ask an expert from your Passion Jardins garden centre more about the subject. There are so many uses for these shrubs that evolve into a hedge and help you feel more at home in your yard.

Buxus microphylla 'Green Velvet'
'Green Velvet' Boxwood

⬍ 100 cm   ⬌ 100 cm   ❄ ☀ ⛅ ZONE 5 🦌

Lovely compact shrub with evergreen leaves, perfect for creating short formal hedges. Plant in a spot protected from the wind, in light, moderately rich, cool, well-drained soil.

Cornus alba 'Ivory Halo'
'Ivory Halo' Tartarian Dogwood

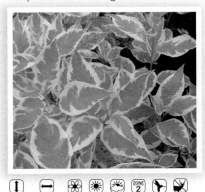

⬍ 150 cm   ⬌ 100-150 cm   5   ❄ ☀ ⛅ ZONE 2 🐦 🦌

Beautiful luxuriant, dense hedge with creamy white variegated foliage. Very tolerant of pruning. Plant in poor, light or heavy, acid or alkaline and slightly moist soil.

Caragana arborescens
Siberian Peashrub

⬍ 400 cm   ⬌ 100-200 cm   5   ❄ ☀ ⛅ ZONE 2 🐦

The best hedge for difficult spots: strong wind, de-icing salts, poor or dry soil, etc. Whether formal or informal, it makes a tough screen.

Cotoneaster acutifolius
Peking Cotoneaster

⬍ 200 cm   ⬌ 60-100 cm   5-6   ❄ ☀ ⛅ ZONE 2 🐦 🦌

Beautiful shiny dark green foliage on a shrub that is easy to prune. Undemanding, it even grows in shade. Does best in moderately rich, rather dry soil.

Hydrangea arborescens 'Annabelle'
'Annabelle' Smooth Hydrangea

🔵 120 cm | 🔲 150 cm | ❄ 7-9 | ☀ | 🌤 | ☁ | ZONE 3

Interesting for creating informal hedges: just let it grow without pruning. A classic! Very easy to grow; prefers rich soil.

Ligustrum vulgaris 'Cheyenne'
'Cheyenne' Common Privet

🔵 200 cm | 🔲 175 cm | ☀ | 🌤 | ZONE 4 | 🦋 | ✂

Simple, unpretentious foliage… but a great, undemanding hedge! Forms a green background ideal for showing off other plantings. Grows in moderately rich, cool, well-drained soil.

Lonicera tatarica 'Honey Rose'
'Honey Rose' Tatarian Honeysuckle

🔵 300 cm | 🔲 100-200 cm | ❄ 5 | ☀ | ZONE 2 | 🦅 | 🦌

The perfect hedge to plant around a bird garden, as the trumpet-shaped flowers attract hummingbirds. Grows anywhere, in poor or rich, light or heavy, cool, well-drained soil. Resistant to witches' broom.

Physocarpus opulifolius 'Dart's Gold'
'Dart's Gold' Golden Ninebark

Our favorite picks

🔵 150 cm | 🔲 100-150 cm | ❄ 5-6 | ☀ | 🌤 | ZONE 2 | 🦅

Hedges don't have to be green! Interesting golden foliage on a tall shrub very tolerant of pruning. Prefers poor, cool, well-drained soil.

Physocarpus opulifolius 'Diabolo'
'Diabolo' Ninebark

(PV)

🔼 200 cm ↔ 100-150 cm ❄ 5-6 ☀ ❄ [ZONE 2] ✂

One of the most original foliage colours for a hedge: dark purple! Reliable plant with no flaws. Even does well in poor, cool, well-drained soil. Just as attractive as a formal hedge as an informal one.

Physocarpus opulifolius 'Summer Wine'
'Summer Wine' Ninebark

(PV)

🔼 150cm ↔ 100-150 cm ❄ 5-6 ☀ ❄ [ZONE 3] ✂

This hedge will turn heads with its dark purple stems and leaves. More compact than 'Diabolo', thus needing less pruning. Does well in poor, cool, well-drained soil.

Physocarpus opulifolius 'Nanus'
Dwarf Ninebark

🔼 1,20m ↔ 1,00m ❄ 5-6 ☀ ❄ ❄ [ZONE 4] ✂

Small compact shrub with small dark green leaves. Makes an attractive low hedge in both sun and shade. Suitable for poor, slightly moist soil.

Ribes alpinum 'Schmidt'
Alpine Currant

🔼 150 cm ↔ 150cm ❄ 5 ☀ ❄ ❄ [ZONE 2] ✂ 🦌

A classic hedge plant. Perfect for short hedges. Very tolerant of repeated pruning. Plant in rich, slightly alkaline, dry soil.

Rosa rugosa 'Blanc Double de Coubert'
'Blanc Double de Coubert' Rugosa Rose

150 cm 120-150 cm 6-9 ZONE 2

Hardy and disease-resistant… and what a charming rose! Very fragrant. Tolerates poor, dry soil, but prefers moderately rich, light, somewhat acid, cool and well-drained conditions.

Rosa rugosa 'Hansa'
'Hansa' Rugosa Rose

(PV)

150 cm 100-150 cm 6-9 ZONE 3

The most enchanting fragrance of all! A big, tough, very disease-resistant rose. Grows even in light, poor or dry soil. Grow as an informal hedge..

Rosa rugosa 'F.J. Grootendorst'
'F.J. Grootendorst' Rugosa Rose

130 cm 100-120 cm 6-9 ZONE 3

A robust, rock solid rose that bears clusters of small fringed flowers. Informal hedge for moderately rich, light, somewhat acid, cool, well-drained soil.

Salix integra 'Hakuro Nishiki'
Japanese Dappled Willow

200cm 100-150 cm ZONE 4

One of the prettiest variegated foliages of all, plus this shrub can take tough growing conditions such as poor, light or heavy, acid or alkaline or moist soil.

Salix purpurea 'Nana'
Dwarf Purpleosier Willow, Dwarf Arctic Willow

150 cm   100-150 cm   ☀   ZONE 2

Attractive and elegant greyish leaves that you can prune to your liking. Super-tolerant plant: use it in poor to rich, light to heavy, acid to alkaline, moist soil.

Spiraea cinerea 'Grefsheim'
Elf's Home Spirea

150 cm   60-100 cm   ❀   ☀   ZONE 4   ✂

An attractive spirea for creating small informal or formal hedges. It does well in moderately rich, cool, well-drained soil.

Spiraea japonica 'Gold Mound'
'Gold Mound' Japanese Spirea

70 cm   60-80 cm   7-9   ❀   ☀   ❄   ZONE 3   ✂

Well known to gardeners, this naturally rounded spirea is ideal for low hedges. To take full advantage of its bloom, don't prune. Plant in heavy or light, rich, well-drained soil.

Spiraea japonica 'Little Princess'
'Little Princess' Japanese Spirea

60 cm   45-60 cm   7-9   ❀   ☀   ❄   ZONE 3   ✂

Very petite spirea with beautiful and abundant pale pink flowers. Ideal for bordering paths in rich, friable or heavy, cool, well-drained soil.

Spiraea vanhouttei
Van Houtte Spirea, Bridal Wreath Spirea

⬍	⬌	✿	☀	❀	ZONE 4	🚫
200 cm	100-175 cm	6				

Even more beautiful when not pruned, especially in the spring when it blooms. Tolerates both light and heavy, dry and very moist soil, but prefers rich growing conditions.

Syringa prestoniae 'James Mac Farlane'
'James Mac Farlane' Preston Lilac

⬍	⬌	✿	☀	❀	ZONE 2	🐦	🦋	🚫	📷
250 cm	150-200 cm	6							

The perfect screen requiring no pruning, it grows all on its own, then rewards our negligence with beautiful blooms. Moderately rich, somewhat acid, cool, well-drained soil.

Thuja occidentalis
Eastern Arborvitae

⬍	⬌	☀	❀	ZONE 2	🐦	📷
1500 cm	60-250 cm					

The favourite for creating a year-long evergreen hedge. Native species that does well in moderately rich, light or heavy, slightly moist soil.

Thuja occidentalis 'Nigra'
Dark Green Eastern Arborvitae

(PV)

⬍	⬌	☀	❀	ZONE 3	📷	🐦
600 cm	60-250 cm					

A selection with dark green foliage making an excellent hedge. Moderately rich, light or heavy and somewhat moist soil. Maintains its colour even in winter.

Conifers

Conifers make up much of the evergreen forest that has always been part of our natural landscape
and they also dominate the landscape around our homes during the winter months. Some are imposing giants and look best on huge lots while others, with more upright or spreading habits, are easier to use in smaller yards. It is however best to avoid planting them too close to home foundations, not only because they are sensitive to frost heaving, but their rather rigid silhouette is not very effective against a wall: the fine texture of their foliage and their blue-green colours are

Picea abies 'Acrocona'

too delicate to be easily seen there. Put them instead in front of leafy shrubs and all their traits will be highlighted. Besides, two plants together do a much better job of camouflaging a home's foundation. Dwarf conifers look better when they are planted by groups of three or five. Another type of conifer to take into consideration are the creeping varieties, many of which are native to Quebec. They're able to resist drought and make beautiful green carpets for all-season beauty!

◀ *Pinus nigra* var. *austriaca*

Chamaecyparis nootkatensis 'Pendula'
Weeping Nootka Falsecypress

A star is born! Graceful weeping foliage on an upright plant. Prefers moderately rich, somewhat acid, cool, well-drained soil. Plant so it is sheltered from the wind.

5,00 m   3,00 m

Juniperus scopulorum 'Moonglow'
'Moonglow' Rocky Mountain Juniper

Add height to the garden with this conifer with dense bluish needles. Grows well in moderately rich, rocky, cool, well-drained soil.

6,00 m   2,25 m

Juniperus virginiana 'Blue Arrow'
'Blue Arrow' Eastern Red Cedar

A real arrow! Tall and very narrow, with bluish green needles. Very hardy. Plant it in moderately rich, rocky, dry soil.

4,00 m   0,60 m

Larix decidua 'Pendula'
Weeping European Larch Standard

Superb weeping habit. The bluish needles become golden yellow in fall before they drop off. Very hardy. Moderately rich, somewhat acid, cool and well-drained soil.

1,00-2,50 m   2,00 m

Larix decidua 'Varied Directions'
'Varied Directions' European Larch Standard

With branches that head out in all directions, this larch attracts a lot of attention! Plant in moderately rich, somewhat acid, cool, well-drained soil.

🡩 🡨🡪 ☀ ❄ ZONE 3 🟦

2,00 m   3,00 m

Picea abies
Norway Spruce

Tall conifer with arching branches. It can be used as a hedge, a windbreak, or a screen. Ideal in moderately rich, somewhat acid, cool, well-drained soil.

PV

🡩 🡨🡪 ☀ ZONE 2 🟦

25,00 m   10,00 m

Picea abies 'Acrocona'
'Acrocona' Norway Spruce

The wine red cones give the branches a somewhat weeping habit. Large shrub or small tree. Plant it in moderately rich, somewhat acid, cool, well-drained soil.

Our favorite picks

🡩 🡨🡪 ☀ ZONE 4 🟦 🦌

3,00 m   2,00 m

Picea abies 'Ohlendorfii'
'Ohlendorfii' Norway Spruce

Slow growing cultivar with dark green needles that always remain dense. Conical, upright habit. Plant in moderately rich, somewhat acid, cool, well-drained soil.

🡩 🡨🡪 ☀ ZONE 2 🟦

1,50 m   1,50 m

Picea abies 'Pendula'
Weeping Norway Spruce

Superb weeping branches. Creeps along the ground unless top-grafted on an upright stem or trained onto a stake. Plant in moderately rich, acid, cool, well-drained soil.

🔼 0,60-2,50 m   ↔ 1,00-3,00 m   ☀   ZONE 3   🐦

Picea abies 'Rubra Spicata'
'Rubra Spicata' Norway Spruce

Surprising! New growths are dark red in the spring. Give it a starring role in moderately rich, somewhat acid, cool, well-drained soil.

Our favorite picks

🔼 10,00 m   ↔ 4,00 m   ☀   ZONE 3   🐦

Picea glauca
White Spruce

Very hardy native tree. Ideal for screening. All types of soil are suitable, from rich to poor, light to heavy, but always well-drained.

🔼 20,00 m   ↔ 6,00 m   ☀   ZONE 1   🐦   🐦

Picea glauca 'Conica'
Dwarf Alberta Spruce

Small compact cone, regular and dense. Plant so it is sheltered from the wind in poor or rich, light or heavy, acid or alkaline, cool, well-drained soil.

🔼 1,50-2,00 m   ↔ 0,80-1,00 m   ☀   ZONE 4   🐦

Picea glauca 'Jean's Dilly'
'Jean's Dilly' White Spruce

Small conical conifer with very fine texture. Ideal in formal gardens or in mixed perennial beds. Tolerates all soils, including poor, light, heavy, acid, cool, and well-drained soil.

⬆ ↔ ☀ ❄ ZONE 4

2,00 m 0,80 m

Picea pungens 'Fat Albert'
'Fat Albert' Colorado Blue Spruce

Squat spruce with very light blue needles, interesting for smaller yards. Best in moderately rich, somewhat acid, cool, well-drained soil. Attractive in small groups for screening purposes.

⬆ ↔ ☀ ZONE 3 🦌 🦌

7,00 m 4,00 m

Picea pungens 'Globosa'
Dwarf Colorado Blue Spruce

The best known of all the dwarf conifers. Low-growing plant with bluish needles that likes moderately rich, somewhat acid, cool, well-drained soil.

⬆ ↔ ☀ ZONE 2 🦌

1 m 1,50 m

Picea pungens 'Hoopsii'
'Hoopsii' Colorado Blue Spruce

The true blue spruce, tall and pyramidal. Beautiful ornamental tree for the front yard or for use as a screen in moderately rich, somewhat acid, cool, well-drained soil.

⬆ ↔ ☀ ZONE 2 🦌 🦌

15,00 m 4,00 m

Picea pungens 'Iseli Fastigiate'
'Iseli Fastigiate, Colorado Blue Spruce

Very vertical and undeniably blue. Beautiful compact variety making a great accent plant. Grow in moderately rich, somewhat acid, cool, well-drained soil. Magnificent!

5,00 m 1,50 m

Pinus cembra
Swiss Stone Pine

Very beautiful dark needles. Upright habit. Likes moderately rich, dry soil. Just as good as a specimen plant as in group plantings.

10,00 m 4,00 m

Pinus nigra var. austriaca
Austrain Black Pine

A pine that will be happy in just about any situation, including poor, light or dry soil. Tall conifer with dark green needles. Can be used as a screen.

20,00 m 7,00 m

Pinus strobus 'Pendula'
Weeping White Pine

Pine with weeping branches. Often grafted onto an upright trunk to give it a certain height. Decorative. Plant in moderately rich, somewhat acid, cool, well-drained soil.

0,70-2,00 m 2,50 m

Taxus cuspidata 'Capitata'
Japanese Yew

Pyramidal plant that tolerates ornamental pruning. Attractive in a formal garden. Use in moderately rich, somewhat acid, cool, well-drained soil.

1↕ 4,00 m ↔ 2,00 m ☀ ❄ ≋ ZONE 4 ⚘

Taxus x *media* 'Hicksii'
Hicks Hybrid Yew

Somewhat columnar, since the branches grow vertically. Good companion for mixed shrub borders. Best in moderately rich, somewhat acid, cool, well-drained soil.

1↕ 1,5 m ↔ 1 m ☀ ❄ ≋ ZONE 5 ⚘

Thuja occidentalis 'Degroot's Spire'
Degroot Spire Eastern Arborvitae

Beautiful pyramidal shape, it stands out due to its slightly twisted foliage. Adds a bit of height to flower beds in moderately rich, slightly moist soil.

Our favorite picks

1↕ 2,00 m ↔ 0,80 m ☀ ❄ ZONE 3

Thuja occidentalis 'Fastigiata'
Pyramidal Eastern Arborvitae

Dense foliage on a pyramidal plant, useful in creating a screen. Loves somewhat moist, moderately rich, light or heavy soil.

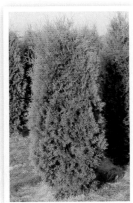

1↕ 5,00 m ↔ 1,25 m ☀ ❄ ZONE 3 ⚘

Thuja occidentalis 'Filiformis'
(syn.: *T. occidentalis* 'Douglasii')
Threadleaf Eastern Arborvitae

All the grace of fine, trailing foliage combined with unparalleled hardiness: a real winner! Likes moderately rich, light or heavy, slightly moist soil.

3,00 m   2,50 m

Thuja occidentalis 'Holmstrup'
'Holmstrup' Eastern Arborvitae

Add some intimacy to the garden by planting this plant in a row. Give it moderately rich, light or heavy, slightly moist soil.

3,00 m   1,50 m

Thuja occidentalis 'Nigra'
Dark Green Eastern Arborvitae

Often used in hedges and screens. Pyramidal conifer that grows best in moderately rich, light or heavy, somewhat moist soil.

3,00 m

Thuja occidentalis 'Smaragd'
(syn.: *T. occidentalis* 'Emerald')
'Smaragd' Eastern Arborvitae

Adds a lot of height without taking up much space. Attractive foliage on a conifer. that likes moderately rich, light or heavy, slightly moist soil.

6,00 m   1,00 m

6,00 m   3,00 m

Thuja occidentalis 'Sunkist'
'Sunkist' Eastern Arborvitae

Wide shrub with golden yellow tips. Takes on a orange yellow coloration in fall. Plant with green foliage conifers in moderately rich, light or heavy, slightly moist soil.

1,50 m   1,20 m

Thuja occidentalis 'Unicorn'
'Unicorn' Eastern Arborvitae

A veritable arrow, narrow and upward pointing. Use as accent plant in moderately rich, light or heavy, slightly moist soil. Requires little pruning.

New

3,00 m   0,80 m

Thuja occidentalis 'Yellow Ribbon'
'Yellow Ribbon' Eastern Arborvitae

An interesting plant for adding some contrast to the garden. Attractive golden foliage that maintains its colour all summer. Moderately rich, light or heavy, somewhat moist soil.

3,00 m   1,00 m

Tsuga canadensis
Eastern Hemlock

Should be used more often. Tall native conifer with graceful, dark green foliage. Plant in rich, somewhat acid, cool, well-drained soil.

20,00 m   9,00 m

Abies balsamea 'Nana'
Dwarf Balsam Fir

0,60 m   0,80 m

Rounded miniature conifer with dark needles. Easy to integrate into small landscapes. Good in rich, somewhat acid, slightly moist soil. Grows equally well in light and somewhat heavier soil.

Chamaecyparis pisifera 'Filifera Aurea'
Golden Threadleaf Sawara Cypress

3,00 m   1,50 m

Fine slightly drooping foliage with golden tips. A beautiful very decorative shrub that does well in rich, light heavy, somewhat acid and cool soil.

Chamaecyparis pisifera 'Sungold'
'Sungold' Sawara Cypress

1,00 m   1,00 m

Small conifer whose foliage arches downward in fine golden cascades. Plant in a protected spot in rich, light or heavy, slightly acid and somewhat moist soil.

Juniperus chinensis 'Blaauw'
'Blaauw' Chinese Juniper

1,50 m   1,00 m

Shrubby, irregularly shaped conifer with upright-growing bluish branches. Undemanding, it likes cool, well-drained soil.

Juniperus chinensis 'Gold Lace'
'Gold Lace' Chinese Juniper

0,90 m 1,30 m

Add some contrast to the garden with this spreading juniper with golden tips. Grows in all types of soil as long as they are cool and well-drained.

Juniperus communis 'Green Carpet'
'Green Carpet' Common Juniper

0,15 m 1,50 m

Let it trail down over a retaining wall. Prickly, dark green, aromatic foliage. Does well in poor, rocky, somewhat alkaline, dry soil.

Juniperus horizontalis 'Icee Blue'
'Icee Blue' Horizontal Juniper

0,15 m 1,50 m

Selection with bluish foliage and a completely prostrate habit. Needs well-drained, rocky, dry soil, preferably some-what rich. Use as a groundcover or in the rock garden.

Juniperus horizontalis 'Plumosa Compacta'
(syn.: *J. horizontalis* 'Andorra Compacta')
'Plumosa Compacta' Horizontal Juniper

0,50 m 1,30 m

Good conifer for rocky, acid or alkaline, dry soil. Spreading habit with upright branches. Purple coloration in fall.

Juniperus horizontalis 'Wiltonii'
'Wiltonii' Horizontal Juniper

0,15 m 1,50 m

A classic for the rock garden or use as a groundcover. It likes moderately rich, rocky, acid or alkaline, dry soil. Bluish needles.

Juniperus procumbens 'Nana'
Dwarf Japanese Garden Juniper

0,20 m 1,20 m

Carpeting conifer with thick, bluish needles. Ideal for covering large surfaces in moderately rich, rocky, somewhat alkaline, dry soil.

Microbiota decussata
Siberian Cypress

Our favorite picks

0,40 m 1,50 m

A magnificent creeping conifer that is always beautiful and that does well even in shade. Prefers light and rather dry soil, either poor or rich.

Picea abies 'Little Gem'
'Little Gem' Norway Spruce

0,50 m 0,50 m

Miniature conifer that maintains its compact form. Never needs pruning. Likes moderately rich, somewhat acid, cool, well-drained soil.

Picea abies 'Pumila'
Dwarf Norway Spruce

1,00 m   1,50 m

A friend of rock gardens and small gardens in moderately rich, somewhat acid, cool, well-drained soil. Rounded shape, short needles, and slow growing.

Picea mariana 'Nana'
Dwarf Black Spruce

0,50 m   0,75 m

Requires practically no care! A cushion of tiny blue-green needles. Prefers slightly moist, rich soil, but tolerates heavy or light soils.

Picea pungens 'Globosa'
Dwarf Colorado Blue Spruce

1,00 m   1,50 m

The best known of all the dwarf conifers. Low-growing plant with bluish needles that likes moderately rich, somewhat acid, cool, well-drained soil.

Pinus mugo var. *pumilio*
Dwarf Mountain Pine

1,50 m   3,00 m

Best seller! Pint-sized pine forming a flat-topped cushion. Enjoys moderately rich, rocky, somewhat alkaline, dry soil. Very hardy.

Spreading Conifers   233

Taxus cuspidata 'Nana'
Dwarf Japanese Yew

1,00 m 2,00 m

Adapts to all growing conditions as long as the soil is cool and moist. Small plant with irregular branches for use in low hedges or small group plantings.

Taxus media 'Densiformis'
'Densiformis' Hybrid Yew

1,00 m 2,00 m

Shrubby conifer wider than it is tall. Tolerates pruning. Red berries are decorative, but toxic. Likes moderately rich, slightly acid, cool, well-drained soil.

Taxus x media 'Margarita'
'Margarita' Hybrid Yew

1,25 m 1,00 m

Striking lime green foliage that looks stupendous against a background of dark-needled conifers! Happy in moderately rich, somewhat acid, cool, well-drained soil.

Thuja occidentalis 'Little Giant'
'Little Giant' Eastern Arborvitae

0,60 m 0,60 m

Small globular arborvitae that doesn't require pruning to maintain its shape. Tolerates both heavy and light soil, as long as it remains somewhat moist.

Thuja occidentalis 'Teddy'
'Teddy' Eastern Arborvitae

0,40 m   0,30 m

Tiny, cuddly, cute as a button! A small globe with unique foliage. Use in the rock garden or formal garden. 'Teddy' likes somewhat moist, light or heavy soil.

Tsuga canadensis 'Jeddeloh'
'Jeddeloh' Eastern Hemlock

1,00 m   1,50 m

Beautiful conifer with trailing terminal shoots that develop very well in shade. Beautiful cascading effect. Rich, somewhat acid, cool, well-drained soil.

Tsuga canadensis 'Moonfrost'
'Moonfrost' Eastern Hemlock

New

1,00 m   1,00 m

Dwarf form that often takes on the appearance of a miniature tree. Stands out due to its white-tipped new growth that turns green in summer. Globular and compact. Plant in rich, some-what acid, cool, well-drained soil.

Tsuga canadensis 'Pendula'
Weeping Eastern Hemlock

2,00 m   4,00 m

Plant at the top of a retaining wall to take full advantage of its weeping habit. Very happy in rich, somewhat acid, cool, well-drained soil. Sometimes grafted onto a short trunk.

Roses

Rosa 'Strike it Rich'

Roses have held a place of honour in gardens for thousands of years, from Antiquity to modern times. Is it because of their perfume, their beauty, or their natural armour that keep intruders at bay? Whatever the reason, roses are popular and we're always a bit impatient to see them bloom. Because of their great age and their travels all over the planet, roses have quite a history! The genus *Rosa* includes numerous species and thousands of cultivars. Certain roses are very hardy, others more tender, so it's best to ask an expert from Passion Jardins to find a rose adapted to your environment and to your tastes. So-called wild roses have a rustic charm and surprise us with their vigour. They make superb informal hedges for larger yards. Climbing roses of Canadian origin are very hardy and need little care. There are also groundcover roses that create flower carpets both colourful and scented. Take a look at the selection of roses offered by your Passion Jardins garden centre and keep up the tradition!

Rosa 'Dortmund'

◀ *Rosa* 'William Baffin'

Rosa 'Alexander Mackenzie'
'Alexander Mackenzie' Rose

(PV)

🌡️ 150-175 cm   ↔️ 120-150 cm   ❄️ 6-8   ☀️   ZONE 3   🪣

Big everblooming shrub rose that resembles a hybrid tea. However it is actually a very hardy rose of the Explorer series. Plant in moderately rich, light and well-drained soil.

Rosa 'Betty Boop'
'Betty Boop' Rose

Our **favorite** *picks*

🌡️ 90 cm   ↔️ 90 cm   ❄️ 6-8   ☀️   ZONE 5   🪣

Unique bicolour bloom! A floribunda rose that bears large semi-double flowers. Shiny leaves. Quite disease resistant. Rich, friable, cool, well-drained soil.

Rosa 'Blanc Double de Coubert'
'Blanc Double de Coubert' Rose

(PV)

🌡️ 120-175 cm   ↔️ 120-200 cm   ❄️ 6-8   ☀️   ZONE 3   🪣

The pure white flowers give off a sumptuous fragrance. Easy to grow. Integrate this rugosa rose hybrid into flower beds or informal hedges. Moderately rich, slightly acid and well-drained soil. Disease-free.

Rosa 'Canicule'
'Canicule' Rose

🌡️ 50-90 cm   ↔️ 50-90 cm   ❄️ 6-8   ☀️   ZONE 6

Attractive rose with a spreading habit and clear yellow flowers that bloom repeatedly throughout the season. For flower beds or rose gardens in rich, cool, well-drained soil.

Rosa 'Carefree Delight'
'Carefree Delight' Rose

☐ ↔ ❀ ☀ ᴢᴏɴᴇ⑤
70 cm 100 cm 6-8

An excellent landscape rose. Bushy and disease resistant, it produces single medium pink blossoms that turn paler as they age. Rich, friable, cool, well-drained soil.

Rosa 'Carefree Sunshine'
'Carefree Sunshine' Rose

☐ ↔ ❀ ☀ ᴢᴏɴᴇ⑤ ▣
90 cm 120 cm 6-7

Attractive upright shrub with semi-double yellow flowers. Leaves are resistant to black spot. Integrate into flower beds in rich, friable, cool, well-drained soil.

Rosa 'Carefree Wonder'
'Carefree Wonder' Rose

(PV)

☐ ↔ ❀ ☀ ᴢᴏɴᴇ④ ▣
75-120 cm 60-90 cm 6-10

Beautiful flowers, good disease resistance, and attractive overall appearance. The perfect low-maintenance rose. For flower beds and mass plantings in rich, friable, cool, well-drained soil.

Rosa 'Countess Celeste'
'Countess Celeste' Rose

☐ ↔ ❀ ☀ ᴢᴏɴᴇ⑥ ▣
60-90 cm 60-90 cm 6-8

Magnificent orange pink flowers with apple-scented fragrance. Floribunda rose that needs winter protection. Rich, friable, cool, well-drained soil.

Rosa 'Cuthbert Grant'
'Cuthbert Grant' Rose

⬍ 80-100 cm ⬌ 90 cm ❀ 6-9 ☀ ZONE 3 📱

Exceptional! Canadian hybrid from the Parkland series: everblooming and with an enchanting fragrance. Very disease-resistant and vigorous. Rich, friable, cool, well-drained soil.

Rosa 'Daydream'
'Daydream' Rose

(PV)

⬍ 35-60 cm ⬌ 35-60 cm ❀ 7-8 ☀ ZONE 5 📱

Different shades of pink in the same flower. Floribunda rose to display in a rose garden or a border. Rich, friable, cool, well-drained soil. AARS 2005 winner.

Rosa 'Double Delight'
'Double Delight' Rose

(PV)

⬍ 90-120 cm ⬌ 60-120 cm ❀ 6-8 ☀ ZONE 5 📱

A favourite with rose lovers. The immense flowers of this hybrid tea are perfect for cutting. They blush at the sight of sun. Rich, friable, cool, well-drained soil.

Rosa 'Ebb Tide'
'Ebb Tide' Rose

⬍ 60-80 cm ⬌ 60-80 cm ❀ 6-7 ☀ ZONE 5 📱

Unique, very deep purple flowers give a dramatic appearance to whatever corner of garden they occupy. This hybrid floribunda rose does best in container gardens. Rich, friable, cool, well-drained soil.

Rosa 'Emily Carr'
'Emily Carr' Rose

New

120-150 cm | 90 cm | 6-8 | ZONE 3

New for 2007, in homage to the famous woman painter. Magnificent red flowers looking like hybrid tea roses. From the Canadian Artists series, it's a hardy and disease-free rose. Moderately rich, well-drained soil.

Rosa 'Félix Leclerc'
'Felix Leclerc' Rose

New

90-300 cm | 90-175 cm | 6-9 | ZONE 3

New introduction! Tall shrub rose with arching branches and nearly no spines! From the Canadian Artists series. It can be grown like a climbing rose. Disease-free and heat and drought resistant.

Rosa 'Frontenac'
'Frontenac' Rose

90 cm | 90 cm | 6-9 | ZONE 3

Small rounded shrub, it is covered with clusters of semi-double flowers. Canadian hybrid from the Explorer series. Disease-free, it grows well in moderately rich, light and well-drained soil.

Rosa 'Henry Hudson'
'Henry Hudson' Rose

50-90 cm | 60-100 cm | 6-8 | ZONE 2

You can count on this rose of the Explorer series since it is disease-resistant and very hardy. Good subject for informal hedges and flower beds. Moderately rich, light, well-drained soil.

Rosa 'Home Run'
'Home Run' Rose

Our favorite picks

🛈 90 cm   ↔ 90 cm   ❄ 6-9   ☀   ZONE 5

You'll be blown away by these single flowers in fire engine red! Very disease-resistant and always in bloom. Shrub rose that likes moderately rich, light and well-drained soil.

Rosa 'John Cabot'
'John Cabot' Rose

🛈 250-350 cm   ↔ 200 cm   ❄ 6-9   ☀   ZONE 3

The most popular climbing rose! Even without winter protection, it can reach more than two metres in height. From the Explorer series, it is not very sensitive to diseases and grows in moderately rich, cool, well-drained soil.

Rosa 'Hot Cocoa'
'Hot Cocoa' Rose

🛈 100 cm   ↔ 120 cm   ❄ 6-8   ☀   ZONE 5

Beautiful deep, intense red flowers with a velvety texture. Hybrid floribunda rose that requires winter protection. Plant in rich, friable, cool, well-drained soil.

Rosa 'John Davis'
'John Davis' Rose

🛈 125-250 cm   ↔ 100-125 cm   ❄ 6-8   ☀   ZONE 3

Lovely shrub with arching branches, covered in flowers! Grow in perennial borders or train it up an arbour in moderately rich, cool, well-drained soil. Disease-resistant. A treasure!

Rosa 'Julia Child'
'Julia Child' Rose

Our favorite picks

60-90 cm	60-90 cm	6-7		ZONE 5	

Petite floribunda rose with golden yellow flowers fading to butter yellow. Old-fashioned appearance and anis-scented perfume. Interesting for a flower bed in rich, friable, cool and well-drained

Rosa 'Linda Campbell'
'Linda Campbell' Rose

150 cm	180 cm	6-9		ZONE 4

Pure red flowers appear in clusters throughout a very long season. This big rugosa rose is a rock-solid shrub. Moderately rich, slightly acid and well-drained soil.

Rosa 'L.D. Braithwaite'
'L.D. Braithwaite' Rose

100-150 cm	100-180 cm	6-7		ZONE 5	

Lovely dark red flowers, very double with a powerful fragrance. English rose that needs winter protection. Grow in rich, cool, well-drained soil.

Rosa 'Moje Hammarberg'
'Moje Hammarberg' Rose

(PV)

90-120 cm	90-120 cm	6-8		ZONE 3	

A tough rugosa rose with dark pink flowers tinged purple. Intense fragrance and decorative fall berries. Plant with perennials or other roses in moderately rich, slightly acid and well-drained soil.

Rosa 'Moondance'
'Moondance' Rose

New

↕ 150 cm ↔ 90-120 cm ✳ ☀ ZONE 5 🪴 6-8

AARS 2007 winner! Beautiful white flowers on upright plants with shiny leaves. Floribunda rose with good disease resistance. Grow with other roses in rich, friable, cool, well-drained soil.

Rosa 'Morden Blush'
'Morden Blush' Rose

↕ 50-100 cm ↔ 50-75 cm ✳ ☀ ZONE 2 🪴 6-10

Delicate flowers on a shrub that will certainly charm you! Add a romantic touch to your garden with this hybrid from the Parkland series. Disease-resistant. Rich, friable, cool, well-drained soil.

Rosa 'Morden Cardinette'
'Morden Cardinette' Rose

↕ 30-50 cm ↔ 30-50 cm ✳ ☀ ZONE 3 🪴 6-8

Small shrub with deep pink, nearly red, flowers. Ideal for container gardens or the edge of flower beds. Likes rich, friable, cool, well-drained soil.

Rosa 'Morden Centennial'
'Morden Centennial' Rose

↕ 70-100 cm ↔ 100 cm ✳ ☀ ZONE 3 🪴 6-9

A favourite with rose lovers! Hardy and disease-free, this shrub rose bears flowers of great refinement. The branches often bend under the weight of the flowers. Plant in rich, friable, cool, well-drained soil.

Rosa 'Morden Sunrise'
'Morden Sunrise' Rose

PV

⬍ 70-90 cm ⬌ 75 cm ❀ ☀ ZONE 3 🪴 6-8

With flowers of changing colours, this Canadian hybrid from the Parkland series is amazing. One of the rare hardy roses with flowers that are more or less yellow. Heavy bloomer. Rich, friable, cool, well-drained soil. Surprising!

Rosa 'Nicolas'
'Nicolas' Rose

PV

⬍ 75 cm ⬌ 75 cm ❀ ☀ ZONE 3 6-9

As with all members of the Explorer series, 'Nicolas' is hardy and disease-resistant. Perfect in moderately rich, light and well-drained soil. Grow with other hardy roses.

Rosa 'Outta the Blue'
'Outta the Blue' Rose

⬍ 90-150 cm ⬌ 90 cm ❀ ☀ ZONE 5 🪴 6-8

Thanks to the quality and the size of its blossoms, 'Outta the Blue' will certainly seduce all gardeners. Lightly tinged mauve, the dark pink flowers give off a penetrating fragrance. Rich, cool, well-drained soil.

Rosa 'Peace'
'Peace' Rose

Our favorite *picks*

⬍ 120 cm ⬌ 90 cm ❀ ☀ ZONE 5 🪴 6-8

Magnificent pink hybrid tea, ever popular for the colour, size and quality of its flowers. Good cut flower. Requires winter protection. Rich, friable, cool, well-drained soil.

Rosa 'Pink Flower Carpet'
'Pink Flower Carpet' Rose

30-70 cm **70-100 cm** **6-9**

This groundcover rose has proven hardy and very disease-resistant. Its generous blooms make it an unbeatable groundcover for rich, cool, well-drained soil. Beautiful shiny foliage.

Rosa 'Queen Elisabeth'
'Queen Elisabeth' Rose

120-200 cm **75-90 cm** **6-8**

Classic large pink rose, still very much loved. A grandiflora hybrid that requires winter protection. Vigorous rose that requires rich, friable, cool, well-drained soil.

Rosa 'Quadra'
'Quadra' Rose

Our favorite picks

150-180 cm **100 cm** **6-8**

It looks like an English rose, but in fact it's a climbing rose of the Explorer series, which says a lot about its hardiness and its disease resistance. Moderately rich, light and well-drained soil.

Rosa 'Rainbow Knock Out'
'Rainbow Knock Out' Rose

New

90 cm **90 cm** **6-10**

A coral pink rose that is very disease-resistant. Flowers non-stop until fall. Use as low hedge in rich or moderately rich, cool, well-drained soil.

Rosa 'Rainbow Sorbet'
'Rainbow Sorbet' Rose

90-150 cm   60-90 cm   6-9   ZONE 5

White, pink, red, apricot, and yellow on the same flower. An entire rainbow of colours! A very original floribunda rose that flowers non-stop and is quite disease-resistant. Rich, friable, cool, well-drained soil.

Rosa 'Strike it Rich'
'Strike it Rich' Rose

150-175 cm   90 cm   6-8   ZONE 6

Very beautiful apricot flowers with a fruity scent on a vigorous plant. This grandiflora hybrid is new for 2007 and an AARS winner. Good cut flower.

Rosa 'Robusta'
'Robusta' Rose

150-200 cm   100-120 cm   6-8   ZONE 4

Big hardy shrub rose. Simple red flowers with a yellow centre. Use this Kordes hybrid in a hedge, a screen or a background. Moderately rich, slightly acid and well-drained soil. Beautiful leaf coloration, turning wine red in the fall.

Rosa 'The Fairy'
'The Fairy' Rose

PV

60-175 cm   60-150 cm   6-8   ZONE 4

Abundant clusters of small light pink flowers on a plant that can be grown like a climbing rose. No matter where you put it, it looks wonderful: with perennials, clematis, or other roses. Disease-free and very vigorous.

Rosa 'Valentine's Day'
'Valentine's Day' Rose

New

↕	↔	✿	☀	ZONE 5	▣
180-220 cm	90-120 cm	6-8			

Climbing rose with small dark red flowers grouped in clusters. Plant near an arbour in rich, cool, well-drained soil. Take down and cover for the winter.

Rosa 'What a Peach'
'What a Peach' Rose

Our favorite picks

↕	↔	✿	☀	ZONE 6	▣
100-150 cm	60-90 cm	6-8			

This shrub rose is the ideal candidate for decorative containers and smaller yards in rich, well-drained soil. Small, intensely fragrant flowers.

Rosa 'William Baffin'
'William Baffin' Rose

↕	↔	✿	☀	ZONE 2	▣
200-300 cm	120-150 cm	6-8			

Decorate arches and arbours with this hardy, disease-free rose with abundant bloom. An Explorer rose of great merit, it grows in moderately rich, light and well-drained soil.

Rosa 'Winnipeg Parks'
'Winnipeg Parks' Rose

PV

↕	↔	✿	☀	ZONE 2	▣
40-75 cm	30-70 cm	6-8			

Love at first sight! The plant in itself is very pretty, with big dark pink flowers. A treasure from the Parkland series. Requires rich, friable, cool and well-drained soil to develop fully.

The Official Tool
of the Johnson Family

ONE GREAT BRAND FOR ALL YOUR GARDENING NEEDS!

More than 100 years ago, Alphonse and Télésphore Garant first put the Garant name on an agricultural tool. Since then, they've put their name on countless round shovels, rakes, and shears. The Garant brand quickly grew across the country until it became the official choice of gardening tools specially made for the needs of gardeners, amateurs and professionals.

Canada's Official Outdoor Tools
since 1895

www.garant.com

Tropical Flowering Plants
for the Patio

Mandevilla sp.

After a long winter of rest, safely warm indoors, the beautiful flowers of the tropics are once again ready to decorate your patio or balcony. Though they're undemanding, it is important to be attentive and to give them all they require to beautify your summer. A small corner somewhat protected from the elements and excess heat, plus lots of water, some good sun, and adequate fertilization are all the day-to-day care these Southern Belles need. The containers they're grown in should be well drained and large enough so there is room for their continued growth. They are usually raised all on their own in individual pots; however, a few shallow-rooted annuals can join them without doing any harm. These majestic shrubs or voluptuous climbers will form a veritable tropical forest on the balcony. Their impressive continuous blooms in a thousand colours illuminate the patio and perfume the air throughout the entire summer. When fall comes, before the weather cools off, these non-hardy plants must be pruned and brought indoors for a well-deserved winter rest. Although often very needy when it comes to fertilizer and water during the summer, during their resting period, it is best to cut back on all fertilizing and to considerably reduce watering.

Wait no more! Come discover these magnificent plants and let them carry you away to the heart of your own tropical oasis, year after year.

Hibiscus rosa-sinensis

Passiflora caerulea

Abutilon hybridum
Flowering Maple

75-200 cm 45-120 cm

With regular watering and fertilizer, this plant will flower non-stop, even indoors in the winter. Beautiful hanging flowers. Best in container gardens.

Agapanthus sp.
Lily of the Nile

60-120 cm 40-75 cm

Large rounded clusters of usually blue flowers are the drawing point with this plant. Grow in a small container with good drainage. It likes to be a bit tight in its pot.

Allamanda cathartica
Allamanda

75-180 cm 45-75 cm

Sometimes shrubby, sometimes climbing, it will grow both in the ground and in containers in rich, well-drained soil. Water regularly. The flowers attract hummingbirds.

Anigozanthos sp.
Kangaroo Paws

New

45-100 cm 30-60 cm

Curious Australian plant with narrow leaves and bicolour flowers arranged in a long spike. Likes slightly acid, well-drained soil, both in flower beds and in containers.

Tropical Flowering Plants for the Patio

Aristolochia labiata
Mottled Dutchman's Pipe

↕ 150-200 cm ↔ 30-60 cm ☀

Large mysterious flower growing on a climbing plant with heart-shaped leaves. Give it lots of water and fertilizer in order to obtain flowers. Rich, cool, well-drained soil.

Beloperone guttata (syn.: *Justicia brandegeana*)
Shrimp Plant

↕ 45-75 cm ↔ 45-60 cm ☀

Unusual plant, getting its name from the pink and yellow bracts that makes up its drooping flower spike. It does well in shade with hostas and ferns. Always keep the soil slightly moist.

Bougainvillea x buttiana
Bougainvillea

↕ 60-150 cm ↔ 60-150 cm ☀ ☀

Long spiny stems, covered in brightly coloured bracts. It usually blooms at the equinoxes. Magnificent in hanging baskets.

Brugmansia sp.
Brugmansia, Angel's Trumpet

Our favorite picks

↕ 120-200 cm ↔ 90-150 cm ☀ ▦

Small tree to grow on a patio so you can enjoy the nocturnal fragrance of the flowers. Simply spectacular with its long, hanging trumpet blooms. Give it lots of water and fertilizer.

Cestrum fasciculatum
Early Jessamine

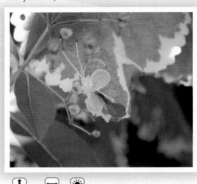

(PV)

60-120 cm 60-90 cm

For continuous bloom, choose this plant with clusters of tubular flowers. Grow in the garden or a container, with coleus and pentas, in well-drained and moderately rich soil.

Clerodendrum sp.
Glorybower, Clerodendrum

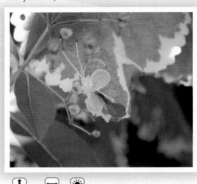

75-150 cm 70-90 cm

Small shrub with big wide leaves. Grow in the garden or in containers on the patio. Constant moisture will stimulate continuous bloom.

Duranta erecta
Sky Flower

(PV)

60-150 cm 60-100 cm

Very resistant to drought and easy to grow. Discover this tropical plant with attractive flower spikes. Some varieties have decorative foliage while others have arching stems. Looks great in a large hanging basket.

Hibiscus rosa-sinensis
Chinese Hibiscus

60-175 cm 60-120 cm

Very easy to grow. The huge flowers of the hibiscus are 100% exotic! Give lots of water and fertilizer and this plant will bloom abundantly nearly all year.

Ixora sp.
Ixora

⬍ 45-100 cm ⬌ 30-100 cm ☀

Superb umbels of flowers, accompanied by shiny foliage. Grows in slightly acid soil, both in the ground and in containers. Water regularly.

Jasminum grandiflorum
Poet's Jasmine

⬍ 110 cm ⬌ 100-250 cm ☀ ⛅ 🪣

One of the most powerful and seductive fragrances that exists. Jasmine develops long stems that you can direct vertically or let trail from a hanging basket..

Mandevilla sanderi
Mandevilla

Our favorite picks

⬍ 75-150 cm ⬌ 45-75 cm ☀ ⛅ 🪣

You'll be buried in the numerous large fragrant flowers of this climbing plant. Use near a fence or a trellis in rich, light and well-drained soil.

Nerium oleander
Oleander

PV

⬍ 150-200 cm ⬌ 75-120 cm ☀

Often grown as a small tree, in a large container, to give a Mediterranean look to balconies and patios. Very tolerant of heat, drought, and wind.

Oxalis triangularis
Purple Shamrock

⬍ 25-40 cm ⬌ 25-40 cm ❋ ☁

Whether alone in a small decorative pot or mixed with annuals, its dark purple foliage always enhances the décor. Small pink flowers appear when the plant is grown in sun. Drought resistant.

Passiflora caerulea
Blue Passionflower

⬍ 75-200 cm ⬌ 75-150 cm ❋ ❋

One of the most complex flowers that exists. This vigorous climber clings to trellises using tendrils. For more flowers, water and fertilize often. Plant in rich, cool, well-drained soil.

Pandorea jasminoides
Bower Vine

⬍ 100-200 cm ⬌ 75-150 cm ❋ ❋ ▦

Grown over an arch, a trellis or an ornamental stake, this plant is covered with beautiful, subtly fragrant flowers. Prefers rich, slightly moist soil, but tolerates drier conditions once established.

Passiflora vitifolia
Grape-leaved Passionflower

Our favorite picks

⬍ 75-200 cm ⬌ 75-150 cm ❋ ❋

Rather unusual colour for a passionflower. Just as easy to grow as the other species, it does best with regular fertilizing and generous watering. Climbing plant for rich, cool, well-drained soil.

Pentas lanceolata
Pentas, Starflower

30-45 cm   35-45 cm

The perfect plant for replacing the traditional geranium in decorative containers. Always in bloom, somewhat drought tolerant and disease-free.

Plumbago auriculata
Cape Leadwort

150 cm   100 cm

Generous plant with bushy growth that flowers continuously, even if it lacks a bit of water. In pots or in hanging baskets, it prefers regular waterings and rich soil.

Solanum rantonnetii (syn.: *Lycianthes rantonnetii*)
Potato Shrub

100-200 cm   75-150 cm

Small tree that bears numerous flowers. Loves full sun and heat and tolerates dry soil. Attractive with brugmansias and oleanders. Rich, cool, well-drained soil.

Tibouchina urvilleana
Princess Flower

75-200 cm   75-200 cm

No one remains indifferent to these flowers with their intense coloration and to their velvety leaves with prominent veins. Easy to grow. Has no special requirements.

Aquatic Plants

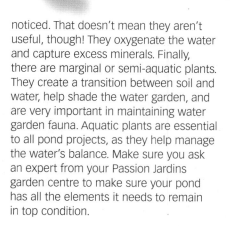

Plants fascinate us by their ability to adapt to all environments, even water! There are four categories of pond plants that participate actively in the aquatic lifestyle. First there are floating plants that meander slowly over the surface of the water and keep it cool. Don't confuse these with emergent plants such as waterlilies: they too have broad floating leaves, but they are linked by long stems to an underwater root system. The role of these aquatic parasols is to moderate the water temperature in the pond. Then there are submerged plants, also called oxygenating plants. They are fixed to the bottom of the pond, but remain underwater, so are scarcely noticed. That doesn't mean they aren't useful, though! They oxygenate the water and capture excess minerals. Finally, there are marginal or semi-aquatic plants. They create a transition between soil and water, help shade the water garden, and are very important in maintaining water garden fauna. Aquatic plants are essential to all pond projects, as they help manage the water's balance. Make sure you ask an expert from your Passion Jardins garden centre to make sure your pond has all the elements it needs to remain in top condition.

Nelumbo sp.

◀ *Nymphaea* sp.

Aquatic Plants 259

Acorus calamus 'Variegatus'
Variegated Sweet Flag

Our favorite picks

🔼 ↔️ ☀️ 🌤️ [ZONE 4]
60-120 cm

Attractive bicolour foliage similar to that of cattails or irises. To make it stand out, grow it against a green background. Marginal plant that can be planted directly in the water, to a depth of 0 to 20 cm, along the pond's edge.

Butomus umbellatus
Flowering Rush

🔼 ↔️ ❀ ☀️ 🌤️ [ZONE 4] 🦋
60-90 cm 30-40 cm 6-8

Beautiful airy flower clusters that stand well above the water. Vigorous plant to grow along the edge of the water garden, to a depth of 10 to 30 cm. Do not introduce into natural ponds.

Caltha palustris
Marsh Marigold

(PV)

🔼 ↔️ ❀ [ZONE 3] ☀️ 🌤️
30 cm 40 cm 5

A true harbinger of spring with its golden yellow flowers. Beautiful clumps of shiny leaves. A marginal plant for the water garden or near a small stream, in no more than 10 cm of water.

Colocasia esculenta
Taro, Elephant Ear

Our favorite picks

🔼 ↔️ ☀️ 🌤️
60-120 cm 30-60 cm

Large heart-shaped leaves. Very pretty when grown in a pot in the water garden. Many cultivars are available, including some with purple or bicolour leaves. Not hardy.

Cyperus alternifolius
Umbrella Plant

45-120 cm   30-60 cm

If you're looking for an exotic appearance, choose this tropical plant with ribbonlike leaves. Does as well as a marginal plant for the edge of the water garden as in a pot set in the water. This non hardy plant can be maintained indoors over the winter.

Eichhornia crassipes
Water Hyacinth

20 cm   30 cm   7-8

It floats freely on the surface of the water, with beautiful, fragrant flowers held above curiously swollen leaves. The perfect companion plant to waterlilies. Grow as an annual.

Elodea canadensis
Canada Waterweed

Our favorite *picks*

30-100 cm   ZONE 3

Essential for oxygenating water even if it is barely visible. Small plant with immersed foliage that can become very vigorous. Warning! Fish love it!

Iris pseudacorus
Scouringrush Horsetail

Our favorite *picks*

90-125 cm   45-60 cm   6   ZONE 3

Very ornamental plant with upright stems, but no leaves or flowers. Grow in containers since horsetail is very invasive in the ground.

Iris versicolor
Blue Flag

55-90 cm **40 cm** **6-7** **ZONE 2**

Fascinating flower created by Mother Nature, this beautiful native plant does well in rich, heavy, somewhat acid and very moist soil. Perfect for streams and as a marginal plant in water gardens.

Juncus effusus 'Spiralis'
Corkscrew Rush

40 cm **30 cm** **ZONE 4**

Original! Narrow leaves that spiral like a corkscrew. Small plant to use as a focal point. Marginal plant for small ponds.

Nelumbo nucifera
Lotus

Our favorite picks

30-100 cm **60-100 cm** **7-8** **ZONE 5**

Spectacular flowers, with seed pods in the shape of a shower head. Not very hardy, this plant prefers container water gardens where water is warmer. Place it in 7 to 10 cm of water. Overwinter in cold storage or at a depth of 90 cm in the outdoor water garden.

Nymphaea sp.
Hardy Waterlily

PV

60-150 cm **6-9** **ZONE 3**

The star of the water garden, adored for its beautiful flowers that open with the sun. Emergent plant with floating leaves. Many flower forms and colours and also various foliage types are available.

Nymphaea sp.
Dayblooming Tropical Waterlily

60-120 cm   7-9

How could you possibly get along without its blossoms? Tropical waterlilies often have more refined, fragrant flowers than hardy waterlilies. Their flowers open early in the morning and close at the end of the afternoon.

Nymphaea sp.
Nightblooming Tropical Waterlilies

60-100 cm   7-9

Beautiful flowers that open as soon as the sun sets and close the next morning. There are many cultivars of interest for the night garden located near the patio or a well-lit path. Not hardy.

Pistia stratiotes
Water Lettuce

10 cm   15-30 cm

Curious lettuce-like plant that floats freely on the surface of the water. Useful for filtering water, it can be used both in in-ground water gardens and container water gardens. Annual plant.

Pontederia cordata
Pickerelweed

60 cm   60 cm   7-8   ZONE 3

Looking for decorative bloom for the water garden? This edging plant grows in small groups and produces spikes of purple flowers. Plant in calm conditions in 10 to 30 cm of water.

Sagittaria sagittifolia
Arrowhead

| ↕ | ↔ | ❋ | ☀ | ☼ | ZONE 4 |
60-90 cm 30 cm 7-8

Beautiful marginal plant. Easy to control, easy to grow and decorative. Readily recognized by its foliage in the shape on an arrowhead. Place in 5 to 15 cm of water.

Salvinia natans
Floating Watermoss

| ↕ | ↔ | ☀ | ☼ |
5-10 cm 15-60 cm

Surprising! This fast-growing floating plant produces a series of fuzzy leaves. Interesting for filling in small water gardens. Not hardy, but easy to grow. Likes calm, warm water.

Scirpus taberdaemontani var. Zebrinus
Zebra Rush

Our favorite picks

| ↕ | ↔ | ❋ | ☀ | ☼ | ZONE 3 |
65-100 cm 45-60 cm 7-8

Always appreciated as a focal point for large water garden or pond. Grow it in 5 to 15 cm of water. Thin, tall leaves striped green and white. Likes rich soil.

Vallisneria americana
Eel Grass

PV

| ↕ | ↔ | ☀ | ☼ | ∿ | ZONE 3 |
25 cm 25 cm

Plant with ribbonlike foliage to place on the bottom of the water garden. Growing completely immersed, it helps oxygenate the water as well as absorb excess minerals dissolved in the water.

From Garden
to Plate

This is the section gourmets like the best!
When part of the garden begins to offer you products so fresh and delicious they melt in your mouth, can there be any greater pleasure? Growing small fruits, fruit trees and vegetables, faithfully accompanied by aromatic herbs, will have no secret for you and you'll even be able to cook up a storm! Discover the flavours that simmer under the sun as well as the wonderful recipes prepared for you by Anne Desjardins of the l'Eau à la bouche Restaurant.

Your garden is generous:
take advantage of it!

Cook passionately and, especially, savour with pride the best your garden has to offer.

Bon appétit!

Anne Desjardins

Fruit Trees

Fruit trees are much easier to care for than most home gardeners realize. But to be successful, no only do you have to know the advantages of the varieties you've chosen, but also what interventions to make and when. The first step is to buy disease-resistant varieties. Your garden centre consultant will be able to help you choose. Visit on a day when there are few clients… you'll be able to get better information.

Another idea you often hear of is that "you need a huge yard" for fruit trees. If standard (full-size) fruit trees like those seen in orchards are indeed very large, the home gardener also has a wide choice of dwarf, semi-dwarf and sometimes even espaliered fruit trees.

When it comes to ensuring the good pollination necessary for good harvests, take into consideration the trees of your neighbours who are within 200 to 500 feet of your yard. There are also self-fertile varieties where one plant is sufficient. In a healthy landscape, it is also important to encourage beneficial insects: they're part of a functioning ecosystem. Of course, organic gardening doesn't stop at your fence, but covers a wide territory of potential contamination. For example, if there is a sick pear tree near your home, there is no reason not to warn, inform and advise the owners, thereby collectively ensuring an environment favourable to plant health. Not only that, but acting preventively and collectively makes it possible to solve many problems which were previously resolved using pesticides and they best to avoid these days.

Pruning advice for fruit trees

Here are five simple questions to ask yourself before choosing fruit trees:

1 Do I live in the right hardiness zone for this variety?
- Certain varieties of apple and plum are very hardy.

2 Will I have the space needed once it is fully grown?
- The rootstock plays a role on the eventual size of a tree: dwarf trees should be reserved for the warmest climates (they are shallow-rooted and therefore fragile). Semi-dwarf trees are fine in moderate climates, while standard trees root deeply and do well even in the coldest climates (zones 2 and 3).

3 Is this cultivar known to be disease-resistant?
- Given the new restrictions on pesticide use, this is important.

4 Does it have the companions it needs to produce abundant fruit?
- Remember that the other fruit trees in your neighbourhood are part of the answer.

5 How long must I wait for the first harvest?
- While a dwarf fruit tree will produce 2 or 3 years after it is planted, a standard apple tree may take 8 years or more

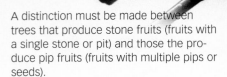

A distinction must be made between trees that produce stone fruits (fruits with a single stone or pit) and those the produce pip fruits (fruits with multiple pips or seeds).

While pip fruit trees are very tolerant of pruning which is even beneficial in ensuring a yearly harvest, that is not the case of stone fruits.

Stone fruit trees are much more fragile and should only be pruned with great care. They'll require initial training, but afterward, only very light maintenance pruning will be needed to eliminate, for example, branches that are badly-positioned, too low, cross, or damage others.

Stone fruit trees: cherries – plums – apricots…

Pip fruit trees: apples – pears…

When pruning diseased branches, it is vital to disinfect the tools (pruning shears, saw, tree pruner) after each cut. To do so, use 70% alcohol. We don't recommend bleach, as it can cause rust.

If the tree is in perfect health, the tools only need be disinfected before and after each pruning operation, but the tools should always be disinfected before continuing on to another tree, no matter what species. In practice, you only need to fill a small container with 70% alcohol and to regularly plunge the tool into it.

Any long branches that are freshly pruned in spring can be forced to flower indoors. Cut the base of the branch at an angle and split it in four, cutting 10 to 15 cm up the branch. Use toothpicks to keep the slots slightly open. Insert the branches in very warm water, adding a few drops of bleach (for conservation and disinfection). Spray the buds with warm water, then cover the whole thing in a large clear plastic bag (a dry cleaner bag, for example). Under the high humidity created, the buds will soon begin to open and the bag can be removed. Place the vase in a cool room, if possible north-facing. Then enjoy!

At planting, make a circle 2 to 3 feet in diameter around the trunk and sow or plant nasturtiums. The succulent

nasturtium leaves will attract any aphids before they attract the fruit tree leaves. Inspect the nasturtiums from time to time.

Each year add compost to the base of the tree in the fall. Very early in the spring, just before the trees bloom and when there is no sign of frost, plant annual stocks around the base of the tree. With their heady perfume, they'll attract pollinators. Then later you can sow nasturtiums.

Be careful never to abuse nitrogen-rich fertilizers, as they can prevent the wood from hardening off (getting its cells ready for winter) and this increases the risk of cold damage.

Fruit trees need magnesium and trace elements, found in special fruit tree fertilizers.

Rodents like rabbits and meadow voles can kill young trees by gnawing the bark at the base of the trunk. No matter what protection system used (wire mesh, drainage pipe, tree protection spirals, etc.), it must reach at least 30 cm above the maximum level of snow accumulation.

Pears

Harvesting your own pears is a joy that always fills me with wonder. Cultivars well adapted to our climate are now available, like 'Beauté Flamande' pear. Here's my suggestion for finishing a meal on a sweet sour note full of freshness!

• Peel, core, and poach the pears in Quebec-produced mead, let cool, then stuff with blue cheese (Rassembleu, made from organic raw milk from Ste-Sophie, for example). Before serving, roast in a very hot oven, basting with the liquid left over from poaching, until the pears start to become caramelized.

Marvellously delicious!!!

For pollination, it is always best to plant several trees of the same species, but of different varieties. Even an apple tree and a crabapple tree can readily exchange pollen.

On the other hand, a pear tree will not pollinate an apple tree, nor will a cherry tree pollinate a plum tree.

In the case of plum trees, it is even more complicated because of their different origins: there are 3 groups of plums, European, American, and Japanese.

Here is a partial list of apple trees that are worth trying as they are resistant to apple scab: 'Belmac' – 'Britegold' – 'Dayton' – 'Liberty' – 'Murray' – 'Prima' – 'Pricilla' – 'Redfree' – 'Richelieu' – 'Rouville' – 'Trent' – and 'William's Pride'.

Common Name	Varieties	Soil
Sour Cherries	'Evans', 'Montmorency'	Moderately rich, light or heavy, cool and well-drained
Sweet Cherries	'Lapins', 'Stella'	Moderately rich, light or heavy, cool and well-drained
Pears	'Beauté Flamande', 'Summercrisp'	Moderately rich, light or heavy, cool and well-drained
Apples	'Belmac', 'Liberty', 'Murray', 'Redfree', 'Richelieu', 'William's Pride'	Rich, cool and well-drained
European Prunes	'Mirabelle', 'Mont-Royal'	Moderately rich, cool and well-drained

Here a few extra-hardy apples for zone 2 and above: 'Battleford', 'Caroll', 'Goodland', 'Norland', 'Pakland', 'Rosybrook'.

Finally, here a are few cultivars of extra-hardy plums (zone 2) : 'Brookgold', 'Brookred', 'Opata', 'Pembina', 'Pitsin', 'Radisson', 'Sapa', 'Kaga', 'Damas'.

Maintenance Tips and Tricks

These cultivars are easy to grow and hardy. Sour cherries can be planted alone, as they are self-fertile.

These sweet cherries are more fragile and require extra attention. Self-fertile.

Pears are generally very vigorous, so don't encourage their growth by fertilizing them with fertilizers rich in nitrogen. Generally they require half as much fertilizer as apples. You have to be patient with the first harvest of pears which often takes 8 to 10 years. It is important to carry out summer pruning, which means removing the vertical suckers that grow near the trunk.
Only the variety 'Beauté Flamande' is considered partly self-fertile. All the others require cross-pollination with other pears.

Plant scab resistant cultivars such as one of these.
Two different varieties are needed for fruiting, but apple trees can also be pollinated by crabapples as long as their flowering periods coincide.
Prune in spring before the buds start to swell. Pruning techniques for amateur gardeners are quite simple and result in satisfactory harvests.

Self-fertile varieties. Late August harvest for 'Mont-Royal', early September for 'Mirabelle'.

Small Fruits

There is nothing very difficult in succeeding with small fruits! You just need to pick up a bit of information concerning the varieties that are available, their light, soil, and care needs and a few details on how to prune them. A bit of simple regular maintenance will pay off with much better harvests. What memories we have stored in our photo albums: of children with hands and faces red with the juice of sweet, ripe strawberries, raspberries, or currants, or blue or purple after collecting blueberries or blackberries. It's something you never forget!

Small fruits take up little space and will do fine in a small flowerbed or even a patio or a balcony as long as they get enough sun. It is no longer rare to see baskets crammed with strawberries hanging from a pergola or a balcony. Thanks to new disease-resistant varieties, pesticides are no longer needed. If you look around your yard, you'll find lots of spaces that could host strawberries, raspberries, currants, gooseberries, blackberries, and blueberries, but also hazelnuts and why not kiwis or grapes for the table or for wine… and don't forget plants of easy-to-grow rhubarb.

Blueberry Surprise

I adore blueberries: an intense colour, a frank, very sweet taste… and they're good for you too! Here's a simple little fast and easy recipe so you'll enjoy them even more!

8 ramekins

- Fill 3/4 with fresh blueberries,
- add 1 tablespoon maple syrup and 2 drops of lemon juice,
- and rap a bit of fresh ginger.
- Cover each ramekin with the following cookie dough:
- Mix by food processor or by hand: 250 g flour, 150 g sugar, 1 teaspoon baking powder, 100 g non-salted softened butter, 120 ml of 35% cream.

Cook in the oven at 375 °F for about 25 minutes, serve warm with cream.

Hint:
Where possible, buy certified plants that are virus free. Make sure the label bears, among others, the cultivar name. As soon as you have made your purchases, write the botanical names and cultivar names as well as the date and where they were planted. This information will be useful to you later if you need practical and concrete advice.

Common name *Botanical name*	Varieties	Distance between plants	Soil	Purchasing Tips
Highbush Blueberry *Vaccinium corymbosum*	'Bluetta', 'Northblue', 'Northland', 'Patriot'	100-150 cm	Moderately rich, very acid, dry or slightly moist	For best pollination, plant at least 2 varieties, preferably 3. If you only have room for one, choose 'Patriot' which is self-fertile.
Black Currant *Ribes nigra*	'Boskoop Giant', 'Climax', 'Consort'	100 cm	Tolerates all soils, but prefers rich, rather heavy soil	For good harvests, it's best to plant 2 or 3 plants of different varieties.
Everbearing Strawberry *Fragaria ananassa*	'Tristar'	30 cm	Rich, light and well-drained	Finally, strawberries that produce fruits all season. Also called day-neutral strawberries.
Strawberry *Fragaria ananassa*	'Red-Coat', 'Vivarosa'	30 cm	Rich, light and very well-drained	To prolong the pleasure, grow 3 cultivars with different harvest dates: early, mid-season and late.

Common name *Botanical name*	Varieties	Distance between plants	Soil	Purchasing Tips
Raspberry *Rubus idaeus*	'Brandywine', 'Boyne', 'Early Sweet', 'Kiwi Gold'	75-90 cm	Rich, quite light and well-drained	There are 2 main growing methods: in clumps around the post of a pergola or in rows. May or may not need staking, depending on variety's height.
Double-cropping Raspberry *Rubus idaeus*	'Heritage'	75-90 cm	Rich, quite light and well-drained	"Double-cropping" means there are two harvests per season. A small one early in the season and a main one in fall. 'Heritage' is not as prickly as the others.
Jostaberry *Ribes* sp.	'Josta'	100 cm	Tolerates all soils, but prefers rich, rather heavy soil	A wonderful cross between the black currant and the gooseberry. Very productive.
Gooseberry *Ribes grossularia*	'Captivator', 'Pixwell', 'Hinnonmaecki Rouge'	100 cm	Tolerates all soils, but prefers rich, rather heavy soil	Most have somewhat spiny branches. Fruits bigger and more acid than currants. Makes a good defensive hedge thanks to its spines.
Blackberry *Rubus* sp.	'Illini Hardy'	60-120 cm	Rich, quite light and well-drained	Must be laid on the ground and covered with insulated geotextile for winter.
Rhubarb *Rheum x cultorum*		60-100 cm	Rich, somewhat acid, cool, and well-drained	Perennial. Very hardy and popular in vegetable gardens.
Grape Vine *Vitis* spp. *and hybrids*	'Canadice', 'Eona', 'Valiant', 'Vandal', 'Sabrevois'	150-200 cm	Moderately rich to poor, light or well-drained	Prefer the new American hybrids that are hardier.

From Garden to Plate

Names	Growing Tips and Tricks
Low-bush and High-bush Blueberry	To successfully grow blueberries, the soil must have a low pH (4.5, maximum 5.5), obtained by mixing peat moss and sand. Plant low-bush blueberries deeply, setting the stems 5 or 7 cm deep to encourage the formation of rhizomes. Four plants will easily cover one m2 or more. A single high-bush blueberry needs 1 m² or more, depending on the cultivar.
Everblooming Strawberry	Generally it is best to grow everbearing strawberries in large pots and to fertilize them regularly all summer. They love magnesium and iron. In fall, put them back in the ground, either with a good mulch or protected in a spot with good snow cover. Using a mulch and a winter protection fabric will help them survive until the following year
Traditional Strawberry	Create a raised bed so snowmelt water drains quickly in the spring. Be careful not to bury the crown when transplanting. Strawberries can be planted in a plastic mulch to simplify their care. Space them 45 to 60 cm apart in the row. Renew the plants every 4 to 5 years. Buy balls of straw for Halloween decorations, then spread the straw over the strawberries when the soil reaches −50C. You can also use chopped leaves.
Raspberry	It is best to prepare the sector a year ahead so the ground is completely weed-free, as weeds and raspberries don't mix well. Set the plants about 50 cm apart. You'll have to wait 2 to 3 years for a really good harvest. Pruning is easy: after harvest, cut to the ground all stems that already bore fruit. Also, keep only a maximum of 10 new shoots per linear metre. Add 10 to 15 cm of compost in the fall: it will protect the roots and help prevent weeds
Currant, Gooseberry and Jostaberry	It takes about 3 years before you get an abundant harvest. Pruning simply means eliminating old and badly placed branches, cutting them as close to the ground as possible. If you don't dare do it, it's best to do no pruning at all. Plant at about 1 m to 1.5 m in all directions.
Blackberry	Spineless blackberries are fragile and if damaged, the main stem will start to produce new growth with abundant spines. They need a lot of space, as the stems grow several metres in one season. For a good harvest, don't prune the stems, but protect them against winter cold. Flowers appear on the previous season's wood.
Rhubarb	Rhubarb doesn't, appreciate being moved. Correctly transplanted, it grows rapidly if it doesn't lack water. It should be divided only every 7 to 10 years, in the fall. Rhubarb tolerates partial shade, but prefers full sun. Sometimes people suggest you remove the flower stalk, but that won't be necessary if the plant is well fertilized and watered.
Grape Vine	Walls and pergolas facing East or South are ideal spots for growing grapes. The plants need to be tied to their trellis at first, but soon their twining stems will take over. For abundant harvests, lower the stems to the ground in the winter so they are somewhat protected from the worst winter winds. **Spring Pruning**: Keep the new stems that appeared the previous year. Cut back the stems that already produced grapes back to the second eye above the soil. From this eye one or two new growths will become the fruit-bearing stems, then they too will be pruned back to the second eye from the ground. Remember that grapes are borne on the stems that grew the preceding year. Harsh pruning eliminates all chances of a harvest. **Summer Pruning**: When the young bunches of grapes are visible, at the end of June or beginning of July, reduce the length of the fruit-bearing stems. Keep only 2 bunches and the 2 leaves just beyond them. Just cut the stem between the second and the third leaf. This operation must be carried out before the grapes mature.

The pleasure of growing your own vegetables

The wise gardener should, whenever possible, take into account the personality of each plant he introduces into his garden, be they trees, shrubs, perennials or vegetables.

Just like a stylish host, he knows how to place his guests around the table according to their individual interests. His difficulty is therefore to figure out which interest should predominate.

A naturally greedy vegetable will be very happy next to another that is a light eater because it can take advantage of the riches of its neighbour.

Therefore sweet corn, a real glutton, would be very pleased to find itself next to peas and beans. Since the latter are capable of fixing nitrogen taken from the air and returning it to the soil, there'll be more than enough for all. However, much of the nitrogen will not be available until the following year.

To make his life easy, the gardener should set several garden tables, each with plants sharing much the same needs.

Thus, there'll be the table of heavy eaters: the gardener will want to offer them a full menu of 5 kg of compost per square meter.

At the table of heavy eaters, there'll be eggplants, cabbages, cucumbers, squash, corn, peppers, leeks, potatoes, tomatoes and others.

The table of moderate eaters will need about 2 to 3 kg of compost per square meter and will host beets, Swiss chard, carrots, beans, lettuce, peas, parsnip, salsify and others.

One table need only serve leftovers from previous years. It can be the same table where the moderates ate the year before, thus allowing for crop rotation. This year it will host the light eaters: garlic, Brussels sprouts, shallots, turnips, onions, radishes and more…

Once each of these three tables has been prepared, you just have to put the right guests at each one.

With that done, the gardener has yet another task he has to take into account: which plants make good companions…

But that's another story!

Since we reap what we sow, it is important to properly plan the vegetable garden by jotting down a quick plan and adding the name of each guest.

Radishes

Is there a better small pleasure than to bite into a lovely radish straight from your own garden? But I'm sure you delight your guests by lightly frying them in olive oil and dusting them with unrefined salt.

Surprising! Fast! But absolutely delicious and perfect for accompanying a fillet of fish.

Tips:

1 Strangely enough, in a vegetable garden, it is vital to plant flowers. Some people think they're there for their beauty, which is partly true, but there is an even more important factor. The females of certain beneficial insects, like hoverflies and lacewings, need the pollen and nectar of flowers as a source of protein so they can lay their eggs. Therefore sow dill and nasturtiums and add transplants of annuals.

2 Stick a thermometer in the ground before you plant tomatoes. To succeed with tomatoes, which are tropical plants from South America, you have to wait until the temperature of the soil, 4 inches down, is close to 16°C. At that temperature, they still can't absorb phosphorus which often results in the first tomatoes of the season being deformed. That's why it is worth using a thermometer to take the soil's temperature and waiting yet a bit longer, until the temperature reaches 18°C, before planting your tomatoes.

To heat the soil up more quickly, as soon as the soil can be worked in spring, cover it with black plastic.

3 The easiest way to grow nasturtiums is to sow them directly in the garden. When they germinate, all you have to do is to thin them out. You'll appreciate the peppery taste of the flowers and the leaves in salads. They can also be thought of as "living sacrifices", since they can be used to attract aphids away from other plants.

That's why they are often planted at the base of fruit trees. Aphids prefer nasturtium leaves to tree fruit leaves and will leave the trees alone.

4 Carrots don't always have to be orange. In Afghanistan, its native land, they can be purple, dark red, or pale yellow. Purple roots give soups a strange colour!

It was at the beginning of the XVIIth century that the Dutch first selected orange cultivars. Sow your own for more colour: dark red: 'Nutri-Red' - white: 'Arrow' and yellow: 'Yellowstone'.

⑤ There are three groups of tomatoes:

Determinate Tomatoes (D)

The varieties in this group are often compact ones, like mini-tomatoes that can be grown in pots, but others require a lot of space in the ground, up to 9 square feet. Determinate plants are constantly branching and don't need staking. In fact, it is impossible to stake them properly. They tend to mature all at once, so harvesting is done over a short period of time. Several varieties are good for storage, but obviously they do need a lot of space.

Italian tomatoes: most varieties – Standard tomatoes: 'Celebrity', 'Bush Celebrity', 'Debut', and 'Pink Girl' – Cherry tomatoes: 'Patio'.

Indeterminate Tomatoes (I)

These were developed for small spaces. The plants can be grown in only one or two square feet. They must however be staked, as they can reach 5 to 6 feet tall or even taller. One characteristic of the indeterminate group is that they keep growing all summer. As a result, they bear fruit over a long period and their harvest is continuous. To prune them, remove the secondary stems (called suckers) that sprout at the leaf axils.

Italian tomatoes: 'Super Marzano' – Standard Tomatoes: 'Fantastique', 'Big Beef', 'Cœur de Bœuf', and 'Pink Girl' – Cherry tomatoes: 'Jolly', 'Miracle Sweet', and 'Sweet 100'.

Semi-determinate Tomatoes (SD))

This type can be grown either as determinate or indeterminate tomatoes. The best known variety is the old Amish variety, 'Brandywine'.

Vegetable	Soil / Compost	Light	Plant Spacing	Space Between Rows
Garlic	Well-drained, little compost	Full sun	10-15 cm	30 cm
Artichoke	Very rich, lots of compost	Full sun	100-150 cm	120-180 cm
Asparagus	Well-drained, rich in humus	Full sun	40-45 cm	90-120 cm
Eggplant	Rich in humus and potassium	Full sun	45-60 cm	90 cm
Beet	Deep, friable, without acidity	Full sun	10-15 cm	30-45 cm
Swiss chard	Rich in fresh humus	Full sun to partial shade	35 cm	45 cm
Carrot	Deep, light soil, no fresh manure	Full sun	5 cm	30 cm
Celery	Very rich in humus and moist	Full sun	20-30 cm	50-90 cm
Ground cherry	Rich and moist	Full sun	60 cm	90 cm
Cabbage	Well rotted manure	Full sun	20-30 cm	50-60 cm
Brussels sprouts	Warning, not too rich in nitrogen	Full sun	60 cm	60 cm
Broccoli	Rich, average moisture	Full sun	60 cm	60 cm
Cauliflower	Rich, average moisture	Full sun	45-50 cm	50-75 cm
Cucumber	Very rich in humus and nitrogen	Full sun	30 cm	30-90 cm
Squash	Very rich in organic matter	Full sun	30-40	90-150 cm
Shallot	Well-drained sandy ,not acid	Full sun	15-20 cm	20-45 cm
Spinach	Cool, rich in nitrogen, use rotted manure	Full sun, partial sun	5-15 cm	30-45 cm
Broad bean	Average soil, pH not acid, moist	Full sun	10 cm	45 cm
Bean	No manure, light	Full sun	15-30 cm	45-60 cm

From Garden to Plate

Sowing / Period	Planting / Period	Harvest
Not by seed	Outer cloves in fall	Bulbs, in July/August
Sow indoors in pots / Feb. - March	Early May, large plants	Flower bud just before opening, in July
Sow indoors / Feb.	Male crowns / end of April - May	Young spears in early spring
Sow indoors in warmth (25°C) 2 to 3 seeds per pot in March	Warm soil / early June, mulch	When fruit is well coloured
Direct sow / May	Mid April to end of June	Root, in Aug. and Sept.
Sow indoors 2 to 4 seeds per 4" pot April	Plants in early May	Leaves, throughout the season
Direct sow every 2 to 3 weeks May - end of June	-	Root, in Sept. and Oct.
Sow indoors in tray – end of Feb. - needs light	In June	Leaf petioles, as needed throughout the summer
Sow indoors 2 to 3 seeds per pot mid March	Early June, dislikes cold, Mulch	Fruit, as soon as it falls to the ground
Sow indoors in pots, keep cool (10 to 15°C) April	Transplant end of May	Whole cabbage just before first frost
Sow indoors in pots, cool (10 to 15°C) April, or direct sow end April	Transplant end of April	Small sprouts along stem when they reach right size
Sow indoors in pots, cool (10 to 15°C) April, or direct sow in May – June	Transplant mid April	Cut as they ripen
Sow indoors in pots, keep cool (10 to 15°C), April	Transplant mid April, direct sow in May	Harvest as they ripen
Sow indoors in biodegradable pots in April or direct sow in May	Plant with pot in early June, mulch	Fruit, all summer
Sow indoors 3 seeds per pot in mid May, keep warm (25°C) or direct sow in June	Transplant in June	Fruit, from Aug. to Oct.
	Plant bulbs, raised bed	Bulb, when leaves have yellowed
Direct sow every 15 days, April	Transplant very early, before heat	Leaves, as needed
Direct sow 4 to 5 cm deep, mid April	Quite tolerant of cold temperatures	Mature pods
Direct sow in rows or seed hills every 3 weeks, end May - June		Pods, when they are ready

Vegetable	Soil / Compost	Light	Plant Spacing	Space Between Rows
Lettuce	Average, enriched in rotted compost	Full sun, partial sun	15-30 cm	30-45 cm
Corn	Rich in organic matter	Full sun	25 cm	75 cm
Melon	Very rich in compost	Full sun	30 cm	120 cm
Turnip	No compost, sandy and cool	Full sun, partial sun	5-10 cm	40 cm
Onion	Little compost, 1 to 3 kg /m²	Full sun	10-15 cm	30 cm
Parsnip	Friable, little compost, cool	Full sun	5-15 cm	40 cm
Leek	Rich in organic matter, mycorrhizal fungi	Full sun, partial sun	10-15 cm	30-45 cm
Pea	3 to 4 year rotation, no compost	Full sun, partial sun	5-15 cm	45-70 cm
Pepper	Rich in humus, 5 kg and more per m²	Full sun	45 cm	65 cm
Potato	Rich in organic matter, friable, sandy soil	Full sun	30 cm	60 cm
Radish	Light, cool, avoid too much nitrogen	Full sun	5 cm	20-30 cm
Tomato	Rich, but not too much nitrogen	Full sun	50-100 cm	50-125 cm
Jerusalem artichoke	Poor sandy soil, pH 7	Full sun, partial sun	40 cm	70 cm

Sowing / Period	Planting / Period	Harvest
Sow indoors in tray, early April, direct sow in May	Transplant very early, end of April	Leaves, as needed, throughout summer
Direct sow in 4 to 5 rows for best pollination, mid May to mid June depending on cultivar		Cobs, when grains are swollen, starting in July
Sow indoors 2 to 4 seeds par pot, then thin	Plant with pot in June, hill up and mulch	Very dark, mature fruit, when leaves begin to dry
Direct sow in rows, mid April, sow end of June for storage		Well developed root, in fall
Sow indoors in rows in tray, temp. 10°C	Transplant end May or plant onion sets	Bulb, after the leaves have yellowed
Direct sow in rows like carrots. Germination often irregular		Roots in fall, do not cut crown at harvest
Sow indoors in tray in early March at 10°C or direct sow in April-May	Transplant end April or May, hill plants up	Whole plant, starting in Aug.
Direct sow very early, end April – May, 5 cm deep		Pods, when the peas feel swollen, towards July
Sow indoors 3 to 4 seeds per pot, mid March	Under tunnel or cloche or plant out in early June	Fruit, at desired colour
	Canada-certified egg-size tuber, sprout indoors in warmth, plant out in May	Tubers, 2 weeks after leaves yellow
Direct sow every 2 weeks, end of April to July		Bulbous root, early in season, before it goes to seed, in 3 to 4 weeks depending on cultivar
Sow indoors in pots mid March at 15°C, light required	Under cloche or tunnel in mid May or plant out early June	Fruit, when mature to touch, from July to frost
	Tuber, very invasive, plant fall or spring	

Herbs

The increasing interest in health products, exotic cuisine, and do-it-yourself projects has led the home gardener to test new experiences and to try unknown varieties.

The popularity of herbs has been growing rapidly over the last few years and it isn't rare to find in home gardens little-known plants that deserve to be better known.

Consider the taste of Vietnamese cilantro, for example, or the beauty of purple basil, or the fresh odour of lemon verbena.

Both indoors and out, aromatic herbs offer the possibility of combining colours, textures, perfumes, and flavours. From now on you'll find a wide variety of these plants in garden centres and nurseries.

Nothing is easier that putting a container overflowing with herbs on a balcony, a terrace, a patio, and even in a small vegetable bed.

If you don't have the minimum installations necessary to start your own plants or if, as they say, your thumb isn't that green, not to worry: nurseries have taken care of everything. They've even prepared beautiful arrangements in clay pots, hanging baskets and flowerboxes.

Although most aromatic plants require full sun, eight hours of sun daily (partial shade) will still allow them to produce their wonderful perfumes.

If all you have is shade, you can still buy mature plants, use them rapidly, and then renew your purchases.

Tips and Tricks

There are herbs for all soils and all environments. If certain herbs look for direct sun and grow in chalky soils, others grow in rocky, dry soils under a burning sun. Unfortunately there aren't many herbs that dream of a shady corner, beside the freshness of a babbling brook.

It therefore won't be easy for mint to grow next to thyme…

To get the best out of each aromatic herb, you must place them in the spots that suit their specific personalities.

Confined all together in the same spot (like a flowerbox, a flowerbed, strawberry jar, etc.), they won't be able to exhale their full delicacy that is of such interest to the gourmet.

In general, essential oils develop best in a hot, dry environment while alkaloid plants really only come into their own in moist soil.

Some herbs are very proud, even arrogant, and don't like to share their territory: absinthe is one. Others, like thyme, sage, and oregano will grow perfectly well in poor, stony soil in burning sun.

Vietnamese Cilantro

Fresh herbs add an essential touch to the dishes you cook daily. Vietnamese cilantro is one I discovered a few years ago and it has become an indispensable herb in my recipe for scallop tartare.

As an appetizer for 4 people

- 250 g fresh raw scallops, trimmed and diced
- 1 teaspoon Dijon mustard
- 2 stems of green onion, sliced thin
- 3 tablespoons chopped Vietnamese cilantro leaves
- 1 lime, peel and juice
- 1 tablespoon virgin olive oil
- Salt to taste
- Tabasco sauce

Mix all the ingredients 10 minutes before serving with a fine cucumber julienne.

The garden is like a huge table. We as gardeners invite the herbs of the entire world to spend their warm season within our walls and gardens, so here are some helpful hints to make sure they spend a pleasant summer.

Name	Botanical Name	Annual (A), Biennial (B) or Perennial (P)	H cm	L cm	Light	
'Genovese' Basil	*Ocimum basilicum* 'Genovese'	A	60	30-45	S	
'Mammouth' Basil	*Ocimum basilicum* 'Mammouth'	A	30-60	30	S	
'Purple Ruffles' Basil	*Ocimum basilicum* 'Purple Ruffles'	A	60	30	S	
German Chamomile	*Matricaria recutita*	A	40-60	20	S	
Chervil	*Anthriscus cereifolium*	A	30-50	20	S, PSh	
Chives	*Allium schoenoprasum*	P	30	25	S, PSh	
Garlic Chives	*Allium tuberosum*	P	45	30	S, PSh	
Coriander, Cilantro	*Coriandrum sativum*	A	45-50	25-30	S, PSh	

Notes	Utilisations
Italian type. Rich, aerated, well-drained, hot soil in sun. Suppress flowers. Also for containers.	Genovese basil has a more discrete aroma than most other basils. It is used in sauces, with vegetables and grilled meats and to aromatize vinegar. The ideal companion plant for tomatoes.
Very large-leaved cultivar. Rich, moist, slightly acid soil.	A basil with huge leaves, easy to use in preparing pesto. Also for spaghetti sauce
Purple leaves. Pinch stems to obtain a well branched plant.. Does well in a large pot.	Has a much milder flavour that other purple basils like 'Dark Opal' and 'Red Rubin'.
Well-drained soil in full sun.	German chamomile is mostly used in herbal teas. The flowers are usually employed, although some also use the leaves. Interesting as an edging plant. Chamomile essence stimulates the rejuvenation of the liver.
Make several sowings per season... Rich moist soil Partial shade.	Use the leaves in: cream-based soups, gravies, salads, carrots, eggs, smoked fish, chicken, and vinegar. Note: don't mix with lemon.
Divide regularly to produce small clumps: this helps prevent mouldy odour.	Use the leaves with: salads, eggs, dips, soups, aromatic butters, and salad dressings. Use the flowers to decorate salads and salad dressings.
Divide frequently. Prefers slightly acid soil. Rich soil.	Use the leaves with: salads, eggs, pasta, dips, soups, garlic butter, and salad dressings. Use the flowers to decorate salads and salad dressings. Very popular in oriental cooking.
Fertile, well-drained, light soil. Keep quite moist: must not lack water. Re-sow frequently. Dislikes heat. Tolerates light shade in summer.	The essential oils of coriander have much the same properties as those of dill. The leaves aromatize sauces, vegetables and meats. Very popular in oriental cooking. In fact, often called Chinese parsley. The dried seeds can be used like pepper.

Name	Botanical Name	Annual (A), Biennial (B) or Perennial (P)	H cm	L cm	Light	
Vietnamese Cilantro	*Polygonum odoratum*	A P	30-50	40-60	PSh, Sh	
Gardencress Pepperweed	*Lepidium sativum*	A	10-15	15	PSh Sh	
French Tarragon	*Artemisia dracunculus*	P	100	50-60	S, PSh	
Fennel	*Foeniculum vulgare*	A	150	40-100	S	
Curry-scented Everlasting	*Helichrysum angustifolium*	A	20-40	20-40	S	
Bay Leaf	*Laurus nobilis*	P	40-150	20-100	S PSh	
English Lavender	*Lavandula angustifolia*	P	30-75	30-45	S	
Lovage	*Levisticum officinalis*	P	150-200	100	S PSh	

From Garden to Plate

Notes	Utilisations
Rich, moist soil in partial shade. Prune regularly for good branching. Much more heat resistant than coriander.	Looks nothing like cilantro, but makes a good substitute for its aroma!
Grown for its young sprouts. Re-sow every 2 weeks. Consume when plantlets reach 5 cm high.	The freshly germinated sprouts of this little cress are usually used. If grown in the garden, cut gardencress pepperweed down to the ground, then re-sow. Often used in sandwiches with fromage blanc and in salads. Very rich in vitamin C.
Cold-hardy but fragile. Sometimes needs winter protection. Russian tarragon is much hardier, but less aromatic.	Essential to French cooking, it perks up the flavour of dishes. The leaves contain iodine, mineral salts and vitamins A and C. For aromatizing béarnaise sauce. Essential for sautéed chicken! The roots soothe toothaches.
Deep alkaline soil rich in organic matter. After flowering, cut off umbels so seedlings won't invade garden.	Young sprouts used in salads, sauces, soups, and vegetables. Also with fish and sandwiches. Lightly grill the seeds before grinding them.
Difficult but not impossible to root from cuttings. Can be kept indoors with lots of light.	Not true curry, but a very decorative plant thanks to its fine, silvery leaves. The leaves give a very discrete taste of curry to soups, vegetables, and rice dishes. Note: Remove the flowers before serving.
Bring indoors in fall and place in front of a very bright window. Cool temperatures. Rinse leaves. Can reach 1 to 2 m after many years.	Bay leaf is one of the rare aromatic plants which it is preferable to use dry rather than fresh. If used fresh, double the number of leaves may be needed. Leaves keep several days in a plastic bag.
Rather poor and alkaline soil, but especially needs full sun. Not a perennial, but a sub-shrub. Carry out a light pruning, suppressing 20 to 30% of the year's wood. Cover soil deeply with mulch (20 cm).	Much used in perfumery. Has a calming effect. In cooking, use sparingly in fish sauces and pastries. Use sachets of flowers to protect clothing.
Rich, moist soil. Hardy perennial. Grow in the ground. Makes a huge plant.	In small quantities in ragouts and meat dishes. Also in soups and sauces. Since its taste is very pronounced, use only a very small amount in salads… and test before serving!

Name	Botanical Name	Annual (A), Biennial (B) or Perennial (P)	H cm	L cm	Light	
Sweet Majorum	*Origanum majorana*	P	25	25	S PSh	
Peppermint	*Mentha piperata*	P	40-60	40-60	S PSh, Sh	
Golden Oregano	*Origanum vulgare* 'Aureum'	P	20	35	S PSh	
Greek Oregano	*Origanum vulgare* hirtum	P	30	40	S PSh, Sh	
Curly Parsley	*Petroselinum crispum*	P B	30	30	S PSh, Sh	
Italian Parsley	*Petroselinum crispum* var. *neapolitanum*	P B	60	45	S PSh, Sh	
Rosemary	*Rosmarinus officinalis*	P	30-100	30-75	S	
Summer Savoury	*Satureja hortensis*	A	30	30	S	
Winter Savoury	*Satureja montana*	P	15-40	30-40	S	

From Garden to Plate

Notes	Utilisations
Rich, well-aerated, well-drained, hot, somewhat alkaline soil in sun. Tolerates a bit of drought, like other oreganos.	Use the leaves in herbal teas, chopped in salads, sauces, melted butter, and fish. Add a few leaves to meat towards the end of the cooking process.
Rich, moist soil in sun or shade. Very invasive plant that needs control. Very pungent aroma.	Mint tea relieves chills and nausea. It aromatizes soups, vegetables, crudités, desserts and, of course, sorbets.
Tolerates dry, well-drained soil. More interesting for landscape use than for cooking.	To garnish plants. Use as an ornamental edging plant
Adapts to poor, alkaline, well-drained soil, but as with all aromatic plants, its perfume will be stronger in rich soil.	Harvest young leaves for use in pizzas, cooked tomatoes, eggs, grilled meats, and breadcrumbs. Add stem tips to sauces, ragouts, soups, kebabs, and baked fish.
Rich, aerated, well-drained, moist, slightly acid soil. Parsley is a biennial: it flowers the second year. Generally grown as an annual.	Chopped leaves used in salad dressings, sauces, English-style vegetables, grilled meats, and in mayonnaise to make parsley vinaigrette (with garlic). Add towards the end of the cooking process.
Rich, aerated, well-drained, moist, slightly acid soil. Parsley is a biennial: it flowers the second year. Generally grown as an annual.	Leaves are more aromatic and refined than curly parsley. An indispensable herb for cooking and health. Very rich in vitamin C.
Requires light, rich, well-drained, slightly humid, acid soil. Must be brought indoors in fall to a cool, well-lit room. Spray leaves frequently with water	Fresh flowers in salads and pastry garnishes. Leaves for aromatizing sauces, ragouts, fish, and certain vegetables like tomatoes, potatoes, and carrots.
Rich, aerated, well-drained, moist, slightly alkaline soil	More delicate flavour than winter savory. Offers more non-woody material for drying. Leaves added during cooking to dry beans and game. For sauces, ragouts and with grilled or roasted meats
Rich, aerated, well-drained, moist, slightly alkaline soil. Hardy: makes it through the winter fairly well.	Leaves added during cooking to dry beans and game. For sauces, ragouts and with grilled or roasted meats

Name	Botanical Name	Annual (A), Biennial (B) or Perennial (P)	H cm	L cm	Light	
Tricolour Sage	*Salvia officinalis* 'Tricolor'	P	30-60	30-60	S PSh	
Stevia	*Stevia rebaudiana*	A	40-100	30-50	S PSh	
Common Thyme	*Thymus vulgaris*	P	30	30	S	
Lemon Thyme	*Thymus citriodorus*	P	10	30	S	
Lemon Verbena	*Aloysia triphylla*	A	45-150	30-60	S	

From Garden to Plate

Notes	Utilisations
Poor, alkaline, well-drained soil. Dislikes cold and humidity. Needs winter protection to survive cold season.	Use in salads and herbal teas. Leaves mixed with onions to stuff poultry. Associated with cooking rich meats: pork, duck, sausages, etc. With game, in onion soup, and in omelettes. To aromatize vinegar, fromage blanc and butter.
Rich soil that doesn't hold too much moisture. Tolerates neither too little nor too much water. Needs watching.	From South America where native peoples used its leaves as a sweetener. 1 or 2 leaves of stevia are enough to sweeten a cup of coffee. You only need about 1 to 2 teaspoons of powdered green leaves to replace 1 cup of sugar. Stevioside (extracted from the plant) can replace sugar. Important note: The Canadian Diabetes Association does not yet recommend this sweetener due to a lack of studies.
Poor, alkaline, well-drained soil. Dislikes cold and humidity. Plants grown from seed, often called English thyme, better survive our winters.	Tall and shrubby. Use the leaves in broths, marinades, stuffings, sauces, ragouts, hotpots, cassoulets, fish, and baked meats and game. The fresh leaves deliciously aromatize salads and vegetable dishes (especially tomatoes).
Poor, alkaline, well-drained soil. Dislikes cold and humidity. Thymes grown from cuttings, called French thyme, don't always survive the winter.	More creeping. Use the leaves in broths, marinades, stuffings, sauces, ragouts, hotpots, cassoulets, fish, and baked meats and game. The fresh leaves deliciously aromatize salads and vegetable dishes (especially tomatoes). Lemon thyme is also used to perfume jellies and fruit salads.
For large pots in very rich and fairly moist soil. Prune. Place near doorway so mosquito-repellent oil is released by rubbing against it.	Use the leaves for: lemon drinks, desserts, marinades, soaps and perfumes. Freshly chopped, the leaves replace lemon grass (citronella grass) in pork, rice, and fried mushrooms.

Edible Flowers

Since the beginning of time, humans have always used flowers as a source of food. While the Chinese have been dining off lily and daylily flowers for over 1,000 years, the Persians have nibbled on nasturtium blossoms, the Incas on sunflowers and the Romans and Greeks on carnations, sweet Williams and pinks in many of their dishes. Don't we ourselves eat cauliflowers, broccoli, artichokes, squash blossoms, and of course the flowers of many herbs (basil, chives, coriander, borage, dill, hyssop, thyme, rosemary…)?

But have you every tried tasting and using annual flowers, like begonia petals *(B. semperflorens)* in fruit salads, superb marigolds *(Tagetes patula, T. tenuifolia)* in salads and garnishes, flowers of fuchsia, gladiolus, impatiens *(Impatiens walleriana)*, snapdragons, stock, pansies *(Viola tricolor, V. x wittrockiana)*, violets *(Viola cornuta, V. odorata)*, and the inescapable pot marigold *(Calendula officinalis)* in salads with basmati rice and a few pine nuts?

But there are also many perennials with edible flowers, such as the surprising balloonflower *(Platycodon)*, hostas *(H. fortunei* is the best), beebalm *(Monarda didyma)*, phlox *(Phlox paniculata)*, queen

of the meadow *(Filipendula ulmaria)*, mallows *(Malva moschata, M. sylvestris)*, crunchy daylilies and even the flowers of Adam's needle *(Yucca filamentosa)* that make a superb garnish.

And what about the flowers of tulips, like the magnificent 'Apricot Beauty', that, when used as a dish, can show off salmon mousse or sorbet? Finally, there is the queen of the flowers, the rose, crystallized and deposited on an angel food cake…

Warning: Unfortunately not all flowers are edible and sometimes they can even be toxic. It is therefore vital to properly identify them. Your garden centre may decide to display edible flowering plants together, thus encouraging their safe use. However, if plants are sold for ornamental purposes, play if safe and ask the store employees whether they are edible.

Edible Flowers

For more than 25 years, part of my garden has been devoted to edible flowers. Their beauty and colour are assets that stimulate the appetite, but it's through their flavour – peppery, spicy, suave, or flowery – that they make themselves indispensable in my recipes. Their petals will especially spice up a dish of zucchini rice if added at serving time.

Finally, a web site for those who are passionate about gardening

passionjardins.com: it's an inspiring **photo gallery**, a place to get **advice from passionate experts, suggestions for quality garden-care products**, and **circulars** from the retailer nearest you. It's also one way to **participate** in the **"Visit the Most Beautiful Gardens in Europe"** contest.

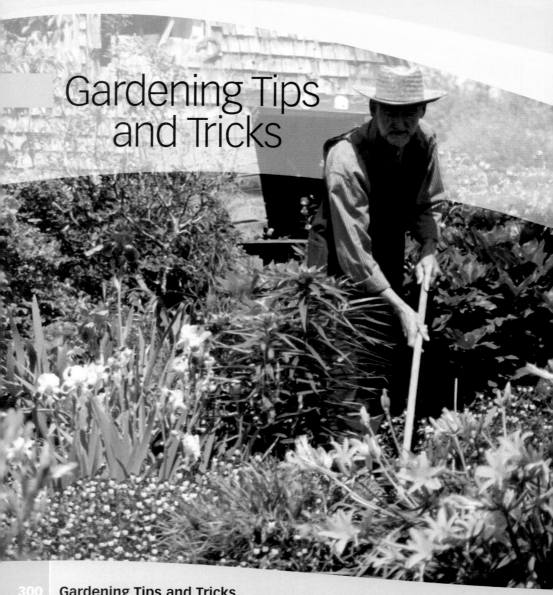

Gardening Tips and Tricks

To help you carry out your garden projects.

Creating a garden? No problem!
All you need are the right tools. But before you pull out your shovel and rake, you should know that by learning to do things the right way, you can save yourself a lot of time and effort! The technical section of this guide offers you precise ideas and detailed explanations that will help you carry out your garden projects. You'll learn a bit more about planting methods, water managment, using different organic products, and efficient gardening practices so you can fully enjoy all the pleasures of gardening.

Choose the Right Spot

Shade or partial shade? Lots of sun and some water, perhaps?
These are the kind of questions that circulate in garden centres, from one display to another, from one aisle to the next, and no wonder! They are vitally important! Paying attention to the vital needs of the plants you buy is the first step in getting them settled in comfortably. But there is a bit more to take into account that just the amount of light a plant needs. You also have to ask yourself about their other needs:

Soil type: This is the texture and composition of the particles that make up the soil. You can amend soil by adding compost or leaf mould, but you can't completely change its composition, at least not in depth. Instead, the best thing to do is to find the soil type, then to find plants that can adapt to it.

Wind Resistance: This is the strength of the plant's structure. Some plants come from open areas and wind doesn't faze them at all! Others, such as woodland plants, evolved in protected surroundings; they may therefore break if exposed to too much wind.

Moisture: This is the capacity of the soil to hold water. This mostly comes from the soil's composition that can allow it to hold water as if it were made up of tiny sponges, but also is comes from the atmospheric humidity surrounding the plant. In the coolness of a woodland, for example, plants lose less moisture to evaporation.

Winter hardiness: This is the capacity of a plant to affront cold winters. It is shown by zone numbers that run from 1 through 8; 1 through 5 in our part of the world. A zone 1 plant, for example, can take temperatures down to -45º C in winter. On the other hand, a zone 5 plant may need a protected spot to survive winters in some areas. It is important to understand, however, that zone numbers are only an indication, as it is possible to change the microclimate of our yards and thus make it easier for so-called tender plants to thrive. The contrary is also true. In a particularly windy part of zone 4 it may be necessary to choose zone 3 plants, which are hardier.

Exposure: This refers to the amount of sunlight a plant needs to live. The usual terms are full sun (at least 6 hours of sunlight), of partial shade (at least 4 hours) and shade (at least 2 hours). It's important to understand that even isolated minutes of sunlight add up, so the number of hours of sunlight is the total for the day. Therefore a plant that receives filtered sunlight through the leaves of moderately dense trees may still pick up enough minutes of sunlight during a day to be considered to grow in partial shade. Sunlight can also be harmful: in protected areas, sunlight can be turned into heat and that can harm even plants considered to be full sun plants.

All the above factors help inform us about the type of environment where one plant or another can thrive, grow and, especially, multiply. These five criteria show that the plant is in the right spot. You can even add a geographical factor! Knowing that hostas and astilbes come from moist, shady forest rich in humus in China and Japan, it will be easier to find in your own yard a spot that resembles the original one. It also shows that each criterion must be put into context. By following only the exposure, you might assume hostas and astilbes would grow best under trees, but under shady but dry conditions, that would rapidly lead to their loss. Moving plants from less appropriate spots to better ones is part of the normal gardening experience and is actually quite enjoyable! When you do find just the right spot for a plant, the entire yard will benefit.

Preparing Soil for Planting

The key to plants that are not only healthy at planting time but that will remain so for many years is to thoroughly amend the soil before planting. The original soil, even if it is of good quality, can always be improved. Amending soil means improving its physical properties (aeration) and its biological properties (nutrients) using various organic components. Solmer Sea Compost is a good example of an amendment. By loosening up the soil, you can improve the distribution of water, air, and nutrients that are indispensable to plant growth. Adding organic matter allows to plants to settle in, to develop a good root system, and to protect themselves against their enemies by outcompeting with weeds and predators.

Step 1: Prepare the Soil

- The entire surface that will be intensively planted, such as a flowerbed or a veg-etable garden, should be thoroughly cultivated, ideally in the spring, although this could also be done later in the season. However, to prevent the soil from becoming too compact, don't cultivate it when it is waterlogged.

Step 2: Work the Soil

- Turn the soil over to a depth of 45 to 50 cm using a spade or a rototiller (for large surfaces). Take advantage of the occasion to rid the soil of roots and weeds, rocks, etc. Next, using a cultivator, break up soil clods to loosen the soil.

- Mix amendments into the top 10 to 15 cm of soil. The following mix works well: compost, peat moss, manure, and fertilizer. Compost and manure are similar in nutrient content, but they don't decompose at the same rate thus prolonging the soil's nutritional qualities. Varying the types of compost used in the amendment therefore enriches the soil over a longer period. Mix equal parts of these composts together: the more varied the menu, the richer the soil. A layer of 8 to 10 cm of organic matter is recommended.

- Also add to the soil Sunburst Quality Bone Meal Fertilizer (2-11-0) or Calcified Bone (0-13-0) as well as Sunburst Quality Plant Starter and Root Fertilizer (12-24-12) following the manufacturer's recommendations.

- For heavy or clay soils, add forestry compost as well as the other amendments. Even when you've carefully amended clay soils, beds that will used for vegetables, flower borders, or individual plantings should still be slightly higher than the surrounding soil as this reduces the risk of root suffocation.

Step 3: Level the Soil

- When all the amendments have been added, rake the surface so it will be as level as possible.

- Newly prepared soils need to rest a while so that they can settle before you plant and put the soil to work. In the meantime, consult a Passion Jardins specialist for help in selecting plants and obtaining practical advice on planting techniques.

How to Plant
with Success

Is it true that you can plant container plants at any time?

Yes, as long as the rootball around the root system is not disturbed. For better results, plant on a cloudy day, especially in mid-summer, and remember that, like us, plants dry out in heat waves and need water! Plastic and fibre pots must always be removed before planting. As for trees and shrubs sold in wire baskets or balled-and-burlapped, just remove the upper part of the basket or untie the burlap covering the rootball once the plant has been placed in its planting hole. Before you uncover the rootball, make sure the collar of your tree or shrub is at the same level as the soil or even slightly higher.

Here in detail are all the steps involved in planting.

Trees and Shrubs

- After you've carefully chosen the planting site, dig a hole whose dimensions are twice that of the pot: twice as wide and twice as deep.

- For balled-and-burlapped trees and and larger shrubs, the hole's shape will be slightly different: you have to incline the sides of the hole so that the bottom is the same width as the rootball. At the soil level, the hole should be twice as large as the rootball. As for the depth, it should be the same as the height of the rootball.

- The soil taken from the hole should be mixed with a quality soil amendment like Solmer Sea Compost, Sunburst Quality Transplanting Mix, or any other organic matter in a proportion of 2 parts soil for 1 part of amendment. Mix thoroughly in a wheelbarrel or on the ground, and add a source of phosphorus like calcified bone to improve root growth.

• When planting a tree, install the rootball in the hole, centering the trunk well, and make sure the plant's collar is at the same level as the soil or slightly higher. Next, fill in about two-thirds of the hole with the prepared mix, then tamp the soil down without damaging the rootball, and water abundantly to eliminate any air pockets trapped under the compacted soil. After a few minutes, when the water has been completely absorbed, continue to fill the hole in, then create an irrigation basin around the trunk with the leftover planting mix. This basin will catch rain and irrigation water, allowing it to go directly to the roots of the plant throughout the summer. Remember to dismantle the irrigation basin before winter.

Planting with an irrigation basin

- It is important not to replace the sod removed around the planting hole.

- Trees need to be staked. Install the stake as you fill the hole in, placing it on the side of the dominant winds. This stake will help solidify the tree so it will root well, but should not remain in place more than one year. Check from time to time to make sure the ties are not digging into the young trunk or branches.

- Make sure you water the tree enough during the first year of planting.

- If the soil in your yard is clay and drains poorly, trees and shrubs will actually do better if planted on slightly raised mounds. Create a mound about 10 to 15 cm high and 15 cm wider than the rootball either side of the plant, thus allowing excess water to drain away. This is important, since soil that is constantly waterlogged will not give healthy roots. If you're unsure whether or not your soil is clay, dig a fairly deep hole and fill it with water in the evening. If the hole drains fully by morning, it isn't too rich in clay and a raised planting won't be necessary.

Planting in clay soil

Roses

- Most roses are grafted, as you can easily see by the swelling at the base of the plant (the graft point) where the branches begin. To make sure that freezing doesn't destroy the plant, the graft point should be completely buried at planting time. When digging a planting hole for roses, therefore, go deeper than usual so that the graft point will be about 10 cm below soil level. For ungrafted roses, an extra 5 cm is sufficient.

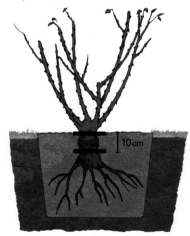

Planting a grafted rose

Planting an ungrafted rose

Planting clematis

Clematis

- Clematises don't like being moved, so it is important to choose the proper planting place. Drainage must be excellent. Plant your clematis on a slight angle so it is inclined towards its trellis and bury it lower than it originally was in its pot: the two lowest leaves should be underground. This practice helps prevent clematis decline from destroying the plant. Add a good amendment to the soil and make sure the plant's base is shaded: the roots of this climber are shallow and can be easily damaged by the burning sun. Using a groundcover is a very efficient way of shading the roots.

Acid-loving Plants and Blueberries

- Acidophilic (acid-loving) plants grow in acid soils, as their name suggests. Plant them pretty much as you would any other plant, but amend the soil with a growing mix especially designed for acid-loving plants. It is important to dig a hole wider and deeper than usual so you can include an extra-large quantity of acidophilic plant soil. That way the plants will readily adapt to their new environment. To keep the soil acid over several seasons, use a sulphur-based fertilizer when it's time to nourish your acidic-loving plants.

Ask the specialists at **Passion Jardins** to point the right products out to you.

Bulbs

- Bulbous plants need light, friable, very well-drained soil, so work the soil deeply while integrating a good soil amendment, then plant the bulbs. The proper planting depth is 2 to 3 times the height of the bulb. Water thoroughly after planting so the bulbs root well.

October is a good month for planting hardy bulbs while May is the best month for tender, summer-flowering bulbs. Group bulbs together to create a beautifully coloured mass planting.

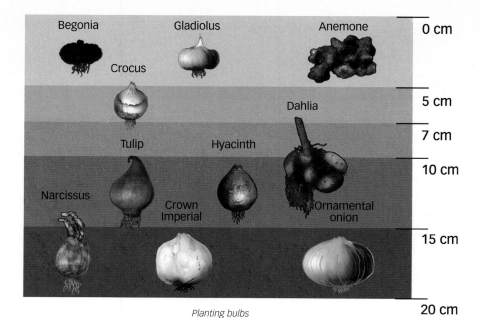

Planting bulbs

The Nature of a Good Mulch

Everyone knows that new plantings need tender loving care! A bit of compost here, a copious watering there, and, more than anything else, a thorough inspection from an admiring gardener to make sure all is well. However, over the last few years, our growing seasons have been increasingly perturbed and untrustworthy, so new plants now need a security blanket, and not just any one! No, this new blanket of organic material is not just for beautification, but an indispensable tool we call a mulch. By covering the soil between the plants in your garden, mulches act on the environment in several interesting ways.

- **Evaporation:** A layer of mulch helps reduce the loss of soil moisture due to evaporation during hot weather.

- **Moisture:** Mulch maintains a certain level of humidity in the soil and thus helps the micro-organisms that decompose organic matter to turn it into nutrients.

- **Temperature Differences:** Mulch forms a protective layer, shielding young roots against abrupt temperature changes and the early deep freezes without snow cover.

- **Weeds:** By covering the ground, mulch considerably reduces the ability of weeds to invade flowerbeds. When weeds do manage to make a toehold, they are easier to pull out thanks to the coarse nature of mulches.

- **Nutrients:** Mulches that decompose return their mineral content to the soil. In other words, plants "feed" on mulch and in fact grow better with it!

Mulches are composed of organic matter, in other words, they are prepared using living plant materials chopped up to make them fibrous and manageable. The smaller the material, such as cacao, buckwheat or coco hulls, the faster the decomposition… and that's a good thing. Another good habit, if you'd rather not purchase a mulch, is to chop up fall leaves and to use them as a mulch. Or consider a living mulch. After a few years using chopped materials as mulch, you can incorporate groundcovers into your landscape. Groundcovers are perennials that form a carpet of green and do the same work as conventional mulch. The advantage of living mulch is exactly that: it is alive. It grows, it flowers and it adds a very attractive texture to the make-up of the flowerbed. Better still, you won't have to add more every year!

Whatever mulch you choose, it is vital that it creates a layer of organic matter between the soil and the air. Forest mulch, made of composted wood residues including cedar, is another good mulch. Don't use a layer of more than 7 to 10 cm of mulch, or water and air won't be able to circulate properly. Avoid wood shavings: they are too coarse and can slow plant growth. Forget too any non-living material: stones, pebbles, lava rocks, etc. They don't help your plants in any way.

Finally, mulches render a great service to your yard, working slowly, quietly, but efficiently. They certainly don't need to be stained exotic colours. Instead, choose the most discrete mulch possible and let your plants play the starring role… or they may give you the cold shoulder!

Maintaining a Water Garden ...Naturally

Water in the garden should be pleasant and trouble-free: we love it for its beauty and its purity. So why not make things simple? Use a bit of good sense, respect your aquatic ecosystem and it will remain balanced with very little input on your part.

As soon as you see the first signs of spring, start the cascade, the fountain and the filter marsh and start applying specialized bacteria to treat sediments. These bacteria that have the ability to digest the organic material accumulated at the bottom of the pond. They are particularly effective in cold water, this is, until the beginning of June.

April is the perfect month for a good cleanup. Put on shoulder-length protective gloves, take the plants out of the pond to prune and divide those that need it. Take advantage of this to fertilize the flowering plants such as waterlilies and marginal plants, even though your plants won't be absorbing the fertilizer for a few weeks yet, not until the water warms up. Have some damp newspaper on hand to cover up your aquatic plants so they won't dry up while out of the water.

At the same time, adding a product such as peat humus to the water helps to stabilize the pH naturally and gradually. It's important to understand that bacteria are most effective when the pH is between 6 and 8.5 and that vinegar or other products that change the pH dramatically in just a few hours have no long-term effect. In fact, they can even harm the aquatic flora and fauna by destabilizing the environment rapidly and brutally.

By mid-May, start to add nitrifying bacteria, overlapping their application with that of sediment-digesting bacteria. If algae start to appear, increase the frequency of bacteria applications to twice a week for 3 or 4 weeks and add a few water hyacinths that will feed themselves from the excess minerals in the water.

Once a month, remove yellowed leaves and faded flowers. It's best to fertilize two or three times during the season. Fertilizer should be inserted directly into the soil at the base of the plants rather than released into the water; that way algae won't be able to take advantage of it. Make the last fertilizer application at the beginning of August so plants will not have any trouble hardening off at the end of the season.

It is vital to understand the difference between the roles of algicide and of bacteria. They're completely different products. The role of algicides is to kill algae… and algae are plants. Therefore, depending on the dosage, the algicide can weaken, harm, or even kill aquatic plants other than algae. Bacteria, on the other hand, are living creatures that don't harm plants or fish. You add them to the water garden to improve its ecological balance.

Throughout this time, keep up the weekly application of bacteria and play close attention to any source of pollution that could stimulate an algae bloom:

- Fertilizer from nearby lawns or vegetable beds;

- Lawn clippings falling into the water garden;

- Fish food: it's a treat for algae! You can stop feeding fish from mid-June to mid-September;

- Run-off water during heavy rains. This can be controlled by installing a drain all around the water garden;

- Aquatic plant fertilizer coming into contact with the water in the pond;

- Cascades or fountains heating up the water.

A waterfall or fountain set in full sun can heat the water and therefore stimulate algae growth. It's best to stop the cascade or fountain during the day, running it only early in the morning, before 9 am and in the evening, after 6 pm. Also, make sure that two-thirds of the pond's surface is covered with plants: this will keep the water cooler.

Other than the action of plants and bacteria, two other essential elements simplify water garden maintenance:

• Adding oxygen. It stimulates bacterial activity and improves the quality of life in the biotope while helping to control algae;

• Installing a "filter marsh" equivalent to 5% of the surface of the pond. It helps complete pond's balance through its biological action.

Come meet your Passion Jardins merchant. He'll be able to advise you on the purchase and use of ecological products for your pond.

Lawns and
Lawn Alternatives

Increasing interest in environmental protection and ecological values encourages us to reflect on our gardening habits, so when it comes to the lawn, the ideal spot for sports and relaxation, it is important to learn healthy management practices. The best time to give your lawn a good base for future development is when you start a new lawn. The secret of a healthy lawn is to give it all the tools it needs to fight off drought and reduce invaders. Whether you're starting a new lawn or giving a boost to an established one, the following advice will help you get the work done correctly.

Seeding

- Before seeding a new lawn, it is vital to understand the existing soil conditions. This is the base the lawn depends on for its very survival and must be of good quality, drain normally, and receive at least some sunlight. That's why a soil test will help you avoid future problems. Ask the specialists at Passion Jardins how to proceed. Before going to the garden centre, carry out your own personal property analysis: what is the orientation of the yard? Is the drainage good? Are there slopes to consider? This information will be extremely useful in choosing appropriate products and soils.

- Good quality soil will allow roots to dig deep into the earth and therefore to better support drought. A good soil mix will also be rich in long-lasting nutrients and will offer good aeration. Poor soils, on the other hand, become compact readily, dry quickly, and encourage weed growth.

- The choice of lawn seeds depends on the number of hours of sunlight the lawn receives. Sunburst Quality Lawn Grass Seed for Sunny Areas requires a minimum of 6 hours of sun a day to grow properly. Sunburst Quality Lawn Grass Seed for Shady Areas requires 4 to 6 hours of sun. Follow the instructions on your seed mix as to the quantity to apply per square metre. If your lawn receives less than 4 hours of sun per day, it would be preferable to consider an alternative (see Lawn Alternatives on the following page).

- When the added soil has been levelled, spread half the grass seed in one direction and the other half perpendicularly to the first: this will ensure perfect coverage. You can sow the seed by hand or use a spreader. Lightly cover the seeds to a depth of 0.5 cm using an inverted lawn rake. Afterwards ensure that the seeds adhere to the soil by passing an empty lawn roller over the entire surface.

- Water with care so as not to uncover the freshly sown seeds. Irrigate frequently, although only a bit at a time, keeping the soil evenly moist for the next 3 to 5 weeks.

- Avoid walking on a newly sown lawn.

- After a few weeks, when the lawn has reached 8 cm in height, do the first mowing, clipping the lawn to 6 cm in height.

Oversowing Following Top-dressing

- The best time to carry out oversowing or even a complete reseeding is between the spring thaw and mid-June or between the beginning of August and mid-September. Do however wait until the soil has dried out before proceeding with a spring sowing. As for fall sowings, don't start them too late: the lawn must be well established before winter.

- In the spring, when the soil has dried out a bit before starting. Remove any detritus (stones, roots, weeds, lawn clippings, etc.).

- Loosen the soil if it is compacted and spread a 10 to 20 cm layer of rich soil mix over the surface: lawns need a minimum of 10 cm of rich soil.

- To re-establish smaller sections of lawn, incorporate one part of Solmer Sea Compost into one part soil mix. You may need to add a bit of lime if the soil is acid or to incorporate some forest compost if the soil is mostly clay.

- To stimulate root growth, work a fertilizer like Sunburst Quality 12-24-12 Plant Starter and Root Fertilizer into the first centimetre of soil. Erase your footprints using a roller, then water the surface thoroughly.

- Sow according to the steps explained above.

- A good fertilization programme will ensure equal growth over many years. Make sure you use products that are safe for you and the environment by requesting Sunburst Quality Organic Selection lawn products.

Lawns are fairly temperamental and react badly to conditions that are less than ideal. There is no use in beating your head against a wall: where lawns just don't do well, look for another solution!

If your yard suffers from difficult conditions such as the following, it's best to try something else:

- Too much shade (less than 4 hours of sun per day) caused by trees or buildings;

- Very hot, dry areas;

- Slopes or steep embankments;

- Areas of heavy foot traffic.

Lawn Alternatives

- Groundcover plants like *Hosta*, *Pachysandra terminalis*, *Convallaria majalis*, *Ajuga* and *Vinca minor* do very well in shady spots. For very dry areas, try *Thymus serpyllum*, *Thymus*

pseudolanuginosus, *Ajuga reptans*, *Phlox stolonifera* or *Lotus corniculatus*. The latter plants will work wonders in hot, dry spots.

- Wildflower meadows are still little known, but for large surfaces, notably in the country, these fields of flowers are magnificent. Ask us about them!

- Organic mulches (cedar, hemlock, etc.) work beautifully under mature trees where nothing else will grow.

- Paving stones or flagstones may be needed where foot traffic is frequent, as lawn grasses can't take trampling.

Come ask the Passion Jardins specialists your lawn questions, as using the right products will always ensure the best results.

Organic
Lawn Care

Do you want a healthy, dense, vigorous lawn? All you have to do is to follow a few simple steps. First, make sure your lawn is well aerated so that water can quickly penetrate to the roots. To test your soil's permeability, carry out the following test: take a screwdriver and press it into the lawn. If this is difficult to do or if you have to push hard, your soil is highly compacted, air is not circulating well, and water isn't reaching your lawn's roots efficiently. This situation is frequent on lawns that have been in place for many years and can result in several problems, like a lawn that yellows quickly during droughts, the presence of numerous weeds (especially plantain, which loves compacted soil!) , and infestations of pests likes white grubs. In such cases, there are simple solutions to the problems, including the following:

Aerating the Soil

- This technique involves removing tiny plugs of soil to that air can circulate and water can reach the roots. You can rent a lawn aerator or hire a specialist to do the job. It's best to water the lawn the day before the aeration so it will be easier to do. The plugs removed are about 15 cm long: just leave them on the lawn. When you've finished aerating, simply rake the lawn lightly to spread the plugs evenly over the lawn's surface.

- The best time to aerate a lawn is in spring or fall, in the same season as you would top-dress or over-sow.

Top-Dressing

- Now that the soil has been aerated, it needs feeding! Top-dressing involves spreading a thin layer (0.5 cm) of Sunburst Quality soil or an amendment like Solmer Sea Compost over the lawn.

Use a spreader and cover the entire surface. This amendment will supply nutrients essential to good lawn growth.

- Using a rake, work this new soil into the holes left by the aerator.

- Top-dressing is usually done in spring or fall in conjunction with over-sowing and aerating, but can be done in any season. It's a good habit to develop as it will help you save water, reduce white grub infestations, and keep your lawn in top health. Ask your Passion Jardins garden centre about renting a soil spreader.

Mowing

- Lawns mowed too short are subject to a number of problems. That's why it is best to mow the lawn to a height of 4 to 5 cm in spring and 6 to 10 cm in summer and fall.

Watering

- Lawns are often thirsty! To make sure they have enough water, before irrigating place a few straight-sided water glasses on the lawn in different areas and check how much water you've actually applied. Lawns need at least 2.5 cm of water each week.

- If there is insufficient rainfall, the best time to water a lawn is early in the morning or in the evening. This will help reduce evaporation so less water is wasted.

Fertilization

- One simple and ecological way of feeding your lawn is to opt for the Sunburst Quality Organic Selection three-step lawn fertilizer programme. Ask a Passion Jardins specialist about the correct use of these products. Good maintenance practices will ensure you have a top quality lawn that will resist even the most persistent invaders. Ask us about it!

The Art of Pruning

Successful pruning increases the plant's vigour, helps it flower better, and keeps it healthy for a long time. The secret to successful pruning is to work from the inside of the plant and not the outside! Make sure you use good quality, well-sharpened, easy to use tools. Passion Jardins experts will guide you to the right tools, according to your needs.

Maintenance Pruning

- There are still many gardeners who think that everything that grows needs a thorough pruning! Yet most trees and shrubs need nothing more than a bit of housekeeping every now and then to remove damaged, broken, or dead branches. Just remove them: it's that simple!

- Other shrubs, especially those with spectacular and abundant bloom, do need a helping hand to improve the quantity and the quality of their blossoms. Flowering shrubs can be divided into two categories. The first includes shrubs whose flower buds form at the end of the summer in order to be

Maintenance pruning

ready to bloom early the following spring. If you prune them in the fall (or too early in spring), they won't bloom the following year, so prune them immediately after they bloom. The second group includes shrubs that produce flower buds during the current season's growth. In general, they flower later in the season, from early summer to fall. With these shrubs, they'll bloom more abundantly if you prune them in early spring. To guide you as to when to prune, here is a table covering the flowering periods of most woody plants.

Shrubs flowering on the current year's wood (prune early in spring)

Aralia sp.
Buddleia sp.
Cotinus coggygria
Genista sp.
Hydrangea arborescens
Hydrangea paniculata
Hypericum kalmianum
Ilex sp.
Kerria japonica
Potentilla sp.
Rhus sp.
Rosa sp (with rare exceptions)
Sorbaria sp.
Spiraea billiardii
Spiraea x *bumalda*
Spiraea betulifolia
Spiraea japonica
Symphoricarpos sp.
Tamarix sp.

Shrubs flowering on the previous year's wood (prune after they bloom)

Amelanchier sp.	*Mahonia* sp.
Aronia sp.	*Magnolia* sp.
Azalea sp.	*Philadelphus* sp.
Berberis sp.	*Physocarpus* sp.
Caragana sp.	*Prunus* sp.
Clethra alnifolia	*Pyracantha* sp.
Chaenomeles sp.	*Rhododendron* sp.
Cytisus sp.	*Ribes* sp.
Cotoneaster sp.	*Rosa* 'Harisson Yellow'
Daphne sp.	*Salix* sp.
Deutzia sp.	*Sambucus* sp.
Elaeagnus sp.	*Shepherdia* sp.
Forsythia sp.	*Spiraea arguta*
Hydrangea macrophylla	*Spiraea nipponica*
Hydrangea serrata	*Spiraea trilobata*
Hippophae sp.	*Spiraea* x *vanhouttei*
Ribes sp.	*Syringa* sp.
Kalmia sp.	*Viburnum* sp.
Lonicera sp.	*Weigela* sp.

Rejuvenation Pruning

After a while most shrubs begin to show signs of fatigue and aging. Fortunately, you can easily give them a new lease on life through rejuvenation pruning. This technique, which consists of removing large branches in order to stimulate the growth of younger ones, also makes improves air circulation and lets more light into the plant's centre. Also, old branches that are slowly starting to decline are more susceptible to insects and diseases, so why not remove them?

Rajuvenation pruning

Pruning Shrubs

- In the case of flowering shrubs like lilacs, pick out a few good, healthy, fully mature branches that are ready to flower the following spring. They'll form the shrub's new structure. Looking carefully, you'll easily distinguish the older branches due to their darker bark. Remove only one third of the older branches at a time, cutting them to the ground. Not only will this rejuvenate the shrub and stimulate abundant bloom, but this kind of pruning will give the entire shrub a more attractive appearance.

- In the case of shrubs with attractive winter bark, like willows (Salix spp.) and dogwoods (Cornus spp.), rejuvenation

pruning stimulates plenty of new shoots… and young branches are the ones that have the best red or yellow coloration. The pruning method is the same as for lilacs.

Deadheading

- The majority of woody plants that produce flowers also produce seed capsules or fruits. In some cases, the fruits are just as desirable as the flowers and should be left on the plant for all to enjoy. However, most shrubs produce capsules or fruits of little ornamental value. In such cases, it's preferable to prevent them from developing, as producing seeds requires a lot of energy and that could weaken the plant. Deadheading therefore helps the plant conserve its energy for next year's flowering!

Pruning Conifers

- The growth point of conifers is called a candle because it is upright and held at the end of the branch as like a candle on a candleholder. In late spring this new growth is easy to see because of its pale green colour. Prune candles if you want to stimulate denser growth. Never remove more than half of the candle. Also, only prune new growth, never into old wood.

- Pines: Prune the new growth (candles) before the needles emerge.

- Spruce, fir, yew, hemlock: Prune while the new growth is still soft.

- Arborvitae, juniper, false cypress: Prune from mid-June on, but no later that mid-August.

Pruning Roses

- With shrub roses, simply remove damaged, older (notice the darker bark), or dead branches. Keep only the youngest, healthiest stems. Don't prune too early in the spring: wait until you can see which stems are alive, that is when new buds appear and the stems become green.

- As for hybrid teas, floribundas and grandifloras, keep only the strongest, healthiest branches. Starting from the base, count 3 to 5 well-formed buds per stem, then cut off the rest, pruning just above an outward-pointing bud. The fewer the buds, the larger the flowers, so what exactly you prune is up to you!

Pruning of shrub roses

Pruning of hybrid roses

Container Gardening, Step-by-Step

Even novice gardeners will find it easy to master the various techniques involved in creating container gardens that overflow with colour and decorate window ledges, decks, and balconies throughout the summer months. All you have to do is to follow a few basic principles and success is yours!

Step-by-Step:

- Choose plants that have the same needs (exposition, watering, fertilizing, etc.). Respect balance and harmony by choosing tall, medium and trailing plants, that is: thrillers, fillers, and spillers. Don't overdo the thrillers, though: one or two per container is enough!

- Water your plants 12 to 24 hours before planting to avoid transplant shock and to ensure they establish well.

- Choose a large container, ideally with one or more drainage holes.

- Cover each of the holes with a piece of nylon screening or landscape fabric to create a barrier that will keep pests out.

- Add a drainage layer about 2.5 cm deep (double that if the container is very large) of gravel, perlite, shells, or styrofoam to the bottom of the pot, then entirely cover this layer with a permeable membrane to avoid any contact between the soil and the drainage material. This will give good drainage throughout the summer, and facilitate recuperating the drainage material year after year.

- In a large bowl or pail, mix 3 parts of My Jardinier Plus Soil + 1 part Solmer Sea Compost, then add Sunburst

Quality Hanging Basket and Window Box 14-14-14 Long-lasting Fertilizer. Mix well to obtain a homogenous blend and moisten.

- Fill the ornamental container with pre-moistened potting mix leaving about 5 cm between the top of the mix and the upper edge of the pot. Leaving this "watering space" allows you to water deeply without risking overflows.

- Arrange the plants according to their eventual spread. Go ahead! Dare to use your imagination!

- Tamp the potting mix lightly around each plant, adding more mix if necessary. Be careful not to cover the plant's crown. Remove any broken stems or flowers that are fully open.

- Water abundantly.

Water, light, good potting soil and applications of varied nutrients are essential to the survival of plants in general. Plants grown in pots depend entirely on you to develop fully. You have to be attentive and respond adequately to their needs.

Maintaining container plants involves checking their need for water daily (sometimes twice a day). Deep waterings with tepid water reduce the risk of drought stress. A monthly application of a fertilizer rich in potassium (K) on top of the slow-release fertilizer added at planting time will be enough to keep your plants in good health. All throughout the summer, remove faded flowers, give the pots a weekly quarter turn (if possible), and inspect them regularly to prevent insect infestations and the spread of disease.

Easing into winter

When autumn points its red, red nose, it's time to make sure your garden gets through the upcoming winter without difficulties. Here are a few helpful hits on how to carry out winter protection tasks, organized according plant type.

Young Trees

- The tender bark of young trees is sometimes seen by rodents as a scrumptious winter treat! Protect the trunk with a white spiral rodent barrier.

- With the root system taking several years to develop, it is worthwhile spreading 5 cm of mulch at the base of your trees to prevent deep-reaching frosts.

Shrubs

- The branches of tall shrubs can be damaged by heavy snow, whether it falls from a nearby roof or is packed down by a snowblower. Bundle them together at about 3/4 of their height using garden cord. Don't pull too tightly: just lightly bring the branches together, enough to keep them from separating.

- Protect plants that are less hardy or that are located in a windy spot by surrounding them with a sheet of burlap. The burlap shouldn't touch the shrub, though: fix it to 4 stakes set 20 cm from the branches. This space is essential in creating an insulating layer of still air.

- For truly fragile shrubs, fill the space between the burlap and the branches with straw or dry leaves to increase the insulation.

Roses

- Shrubs roses are generally very hardy and don't need any protection except perhaps to bundle the branches together so they won't be damaged by heavy snow (see Shrubs).

- Prune hybrid tea, floribunda, and grandiflora roses to about 30 cm and tie their branches together. At the end of November, after the ground has frozen at least once, mound up soil or compost at the base of the plant. A 20 to 25 cm mound is sufficient. If conditions are likely to be hard on roses, use a rose cone as well. Prune as before and create a mound at the plant's base before covering it with the rose cone after the first hard frost. At the first sign of spring, remove the cone on a cloudy day. If possible, plant roses in areas where snow build-up is likely, as this increases the changes of success. Snow was, is, and will always be the best friend of overwintering plants.

Conifers and Broadleaf Evergreens

- Creeping conifers are well protected by fallen snow and need no special care.

- Other types of conifers too are usually hardy and don't need to be wrapped for the winter. However, the weight of the snow, especially heavy, wet snow, can bend the branches outward. By attaching the branches together from inside the conifer and by surrounding them with plastic netting, you can avoid damage to upright conifers.

If globe-shaped conifers are planted near a roof where there is a risk of snow or ice sliding suddenly downward, you can build them a shelter with snow fencing, using it as a roof held above the plant on stakes.

- Broadleaf evergreens, like large-flowered rhododendrons, should be planted where snow really builds up and away from strong wind. In more exposed spots, it's best to wrap them with a plasticized winter protection cover (place the plastic side outward), leaving 20 cm between the textile and the branches, to prevent winter drying.

Perennials

- If your plants are hardy to the zone in which you live or to even colder zones, there is no need to offer them winter protection. However, for tender perennials, those planted near the foundation (where they can suffer from repeated freezing and thawing), or even perennials planted late in the season, it can be worthwhile covering the base of the plant with a layer of mulch or simply fall leaves. Wait until the first frosts before applying any protection.

Climbing Plants

- Climbing plants are usually very hardy: only tender climbing roses and young Wisteria plants need protection. Ideally the branches of these plants should be tied together and lowered to the ground. Then cover them with a plasticized winter protection cover (plastic side outward). Install stakes at either end of the sleeping plants so you'll know where they are when spring comes around!

- Clematises appreciate a layer of mulch at their base, because their roots are near the surface and can be harmed by repeated freezing and thawing.

Hedges

- Recently planted hedges that could suffer from strong winter winds will benefit from snow fencing installed on either side. Hedges planted along streets need further protection, because salt and other snow-melting products, toxic to plants, are often applied to the streets next to them. Use white plasticized winter protection cover (plastic side towards the street) to reduce their effects. By covering the base of the hedge, you can help protect the roots from being damaged by leaching. This problem occurs because salt and snow-melting agents can build up in snow. When the snow melts, the water it forms contains toxic concentrations of salt.

In Short

- Any winter protection installed in the autumn must be removed at the first signs of spring. Wait until a cloudy day before removing the protections so plants that were isolated from the sun all winter aren't suddenly exposed to its full blast.

- Soil and compost mounded up around roses should be removed before buds appear. Take advantage of this step to cut off dead or damaged branches.

- Watering thoroughly in the autumn helps plants, especially those most at risk, to survive the rigours of winter. Don't forget to water plants located near the foundation where rain doesn't always reach the soil.

- It is best to avoid applying nitrogen-rich fertilizer after mid-July, as it encourages the growth of new shoots that are frost-sensitive. Likewise avoid pruning shrubs too late in the season, as the new growth won't have time to harden off before winter.

Visit your Passion Jardins garden centre to find the products you need to ensure your little corner of paradise profits from a peaceful winter.

The Passionate Gardener's Calendar

	March	April	May
General			
Remove winter protections at snow melt. It's best to do this when there are several grey or rainy days in a row	5	4 and 5	2 and 3
Cover the soil with **Sunburst Quality cedar mulch** to maintain even humidity. Depending ont the results of your soil test, add lime to correct the pH	4 and 5	2 and 3	
Add soil amendments and work them into the soil (e.g. **Solmer Sea Compost**, lime)		4 and 5	2 and 3
Weed and cultivate (the soil must not be wet)			5
Irrigate as needed according to municipal watering restrictions			
Water conifers thoroughly in the autumn so they can build up water reserves for the winter. Install their winter protections after the first snow			
Plant spring-flowering bulbs			
Trees, Shrubs and Conifers			
If needed, apply dormant oil spray to control overwintering insects (fruit trees (apples, plums, etc.), roses, etc.)		4 and 5	2 and 3
Transplant or move bare-root trees and shrubs before they bud out		2 to 5	2 to 5

Now's the time to garden! Consult this calendar to learn the ideal season for each action, depending on your region. The numbers correspond to Canadian hardiness zones and appear under the month suggested for each activity. Please note that the dates shown are suggestions only. The right period for doing any garden activity can vary depending on the season and Mother Nature's whims. Wherever you are, enjoy your gardening experience!

See the Hardiness Zone Chart on page 342.

June	July	August	September	October	November	December
			2 and 3			
2 to 5	2 to 5	2 to 5	2 to 5	2 to 5		
2 to 5	2 to 5	2 to 5	4 and 5			
				2 to 4	4 and 5	
			2	3 to 5		

	March	April	May
Trees, Shrubs and Conifers (continued)			
Plant trees, fruit trees, small fruits, shrubs and conifers bought in pots using Sunburst Quality 12-24-12 Plant Starter and Root Fertilizer		2 to 5	2 to 5
If needed, apply sulphur-copper spray to prevent fungal diseases such as scab and mildew (fruit trees (apples, plums, etc.), roses, etc.)		3 to 5	2
If needed, do rejuvenation pruning on spring-flowering shrubs, shrub roses and deciduous hedges. Make sure to remove dead, broken or sick branches as well as any sections suffering frost damage		2 to 5	2 and 3
Maintenance prune roses (dead, broken and weak branches)		2 to 5	2 and 3
Prune summer-blooming shrubs and those with ornamental foliage as well as shrub, miniature and climbing roses		2 and 5	
Prune deciduous hedges			
Prune alders, oaks, honey locusts, ashes, beeches, hydrangeas, mountain ashes, lindens, fruit trees and grapes before they bud out	4 and 5	2 and 3	
Prune trees (catalpas, ornamental plums, horse chestnuts, crabapples) and spring-flowering shrubs (forsythias, lilacs, magnolias, spring-blooming spireas) after they bloom		5	4 and 5
Prune arborvitaes and junipers			
Prune candles on pines (before the needles unfurl)			
Prune shrub roses after flowering			
Prune hawthorns, birches and maples in the autumn			
In the autumn, make sure stakes won't injure the trunk and install spiral rodent barriers			
Fertilize trees and shrubs with Sunburst Quality Organic Selection 6-3-3 or 5-4-8 for flowering shrubs		5	2 to 5
Fertilize conifers with Sunburst Quality Organic Selection 6-3-3 Fertilizer		5	2 to 5
Fertilize roses with Sunburst Quality Organic Selection 5-4-8 Fertilizer		5	2 to 5
Remove suckers and water sprouts from trees	5	2 to 5	2 to 5
Irrigate conifers and evergreen plants		2 to 5	

June	July	August	September	October	November	December
2 to 5	2 to 5	2 to 5	2 to 5	2 to 5		
1 and 5	2 and 3					
2 to 5						
2 to 5	2 to 5	2 to 5	3 to 5			
2 to 5						
5	2 to 4					
			2 to 3	4 and 5	4 and 5	
			2 to 3	4 and 5	4 and 5	
2 to 5	2 to 5	2 to 5	2 to 5	2 to 5	2 to 5	
			2 and 3	4 and 5		

	March	April	May
Perennials			
Plant pot-grown perennials using **Sunburst Quality Transplanting Mix**		4 and 5	2 à 5
Prune dried aboveground parts of perennials and grasses as soon as possible in spring		2 to 5	
Don't cut the foliage of ornamental grasses back in the autumn, as it is very attractive in the winter		5	2 to 4
If needed, divide and replant late-summer-flowering perennials			
Fertilize with **Sunburst Quality Organic Selection 5-4-8 Fertilizer**		5	2 to 5
Cover the base of clematises with **Sunburst Quality Cedar Mulch**			2 to 5
Vegetable Garden			
Sow broccoli, cabbage, lettuce and radish outdoors at the end of the month (mid-April for zone 5)		2 to 5	
Add lime, compost, manure and fertilizer such as **Sunburst Quality Organic Selection 4-7-8 Fertilizer** as needed		5	2 to 4
Sow snap peas, radishes and des leafy vegetables			
Plant garlic and onion bulbs		5	2 to 4
Transplant cold-hardy vegetables			2 to 4
Transplant cold-sensitive vegetables a bit later			5
Stake tomatoes, remove suckers			
Fertilize with **Sunburst Quality Organic Selection 4-7-8 Fertilizer**			4 and 5
Protect plants from ground frost			
Make a final harvest before frost			
Annuals			
Plant annuals and summer-flowering bulbs (after risk of frost abates)			5
Fertilize with **Sunburst Quality Organic Selection 5-4-8 Fertilizer**			
Pull annuals when they are killed by frost. Don't cut the foliage of ornamental grasses back in the autumn, as it is very attractive in the winter			

June	July	August	September	October	November	December
2 to 5	2 to 5	2 to 5	2 to 5			
			2 to 3	4 and 5		
				2 to 5		
		2 to 5				
2 to 4						
2 to 5						
2 and 3		2 to 5				
		2 and 3	1 to 5			
			1 to 5			
2 to 4						
	2 to 5	2 to 5				
			2 to 3	4 and 5		

	March	April	May
Lawns			
When the soil dries out, clean and rake the lawn		4 and 5	2 to 5
In spring and summer, mow to 6-8 cm (except 1st spring mowing at 5 cm) and in fall, mow to 8-10 cm (except 1st last mowing at 5 cm)			2 and 5
Leave short lawn clippings (short) the lawn: it supplies the soil in nutrients and organic matter			4 and 5
If white grubs are present, apply beneficial nematodes for moderate control. Ask your **Passion Jardins** merchant about application conditions			
If chinch bugs are present, apply beneficial nematodes for moderate control. Ask your **Passion Jardins** merchant about application conditions			
In spring, summer and autumn, apply corn gluten meal to prevent the seeds of weeds like crabgrass and dandelions from germinating			2 to 5
Early in spring or in the autumn, oversow damaged areas with **specific Sunburst Quality lawn seed mixes for sun or shade**. These mixes are naturally insect resistant. The ideal period begins in mid-August			4 and 5
Aerate and top-dress with **Solmer Sea Compost** or manure to prevent white grub and hairy chinch bug infestations			4 and 5
Top-dress with **Solmer Sea Compost**		4 and 5	2 and 3
Irrigate regularly (especially during periods of drought) to prevent infestations of pests like chinch bugs and white grubs			
Fertilize. Step 1: Sunburst Quality Organic Selection **12-1-4 Spring Lawn Fertilizer**		4 and 5	2 and 3
Fertilize. Step 2: Sunburst Quality Organic Selection **9-2-4 Summer Lawn Fertilizer**			
Fertilize. Step 3: Sunburst Quality Organic Selection **4-4-9 Fall Lawn Fertilizer**			

June	July	August	September	October	November	December
2 to 5	2 to 5	2 to 5	2 to 5	2 to 5		
2 to 5	2 to 5	2 to 5	2 to 5	2 to 5		
		2 to 5	2 to 5			
		2 to 5				
	2 to 5		2 to 5			
2 and 3		2 to 5	2 to 5			
2 and 3						
		2 to 5	2 to 5			
2 to 5	2 to 5					
2 to 5		2 to 5				
			2 to 5	2 to 5		

Hardiness Zones

Living in a vast territory in the Northern Hemisphere means your yard will go through changing climatic conditions and sometimes some very rigorous winters! To help gardeners better understand the plant possibilities for each region, Environment Canada has divided this territory into **9** hardiness zones, from **0** to **8**. Each number refers to the temperature variations between summer and winter. The highest numbers correspond to areas where winters are the mildest. You'll sometimes also see the letters "**a**" or "**b**" added to the hardiness zone number. They indicate a further climatic division, the "**a**" sector being slightly colder than the "**b**" sector.

You can successfully grow perennials, trees, and shrubs with the same zone number as yours, as well as any with smaller numbers. For example, if you live in the zone 5b, you can grow all plants listed as being zone 5b, plus all colder zones (**5a**, **4**, **3**, **2**, etc.).

Come discover the wide range of plants available at your **Passion Jardins** garden centre, where there is truly something for gardeners in every hardiness zone!

Chart of Hardiness Zones by Region

Alma	**3a**
Amqui	**4a**
Arundel	**4a**
Ayer's Cliff	**4b**
Baie-Comeau	**3a**
Bécancour	**4a**
Chicoutimi	**3b**
Disraéli	**4a**
Drummondville	**5a**
Gatineau	**5a**
Gaspé	**4a**
Granby	**4b**
Hawkesbury, ONT	**4b**
Joliette	**4a**
L'Assomption	**5a**
L'Avenir	**4b**
La Malbaie	**4a**
La Pocatière	**4a**
Lac Brome	**4b**
Lachute	**5a**
Lamèque	**4a**
Laval	**5b**
Longueuil	**5b**

Moncton	**5a**	Saint-Félix-de-Valois	**4a**	Sainte-Thérèse	**5b**
Mont-Tremblant	**3a**	Saint-Georges	**4a**	Shawinigan	**4a**
Montebello	**4b**	Saint-Jean-sur-Richelieu	**5a**	Sherbrooke	**4b**
Montreal	**5b**	Saint-Jérôme	**5a**	Sorel	**5a**
Ottawa	**5a**	Saint-Raymond	**4a**	Terrebonne	**5b**
Pierrefonds	**5a**	Saint-Vallier	**4b**	Thetford Mines	**4a**
Princeville	**4a**	Sainte-Agathe	**4a**	Trois-Rivières	**4b**
Quebec City	**4b**	Ste-Anne-des-Lacs	**4b**	Valleyfield	**5b**
Rimouski	**4a**	Sainte-Claire	**4a**	Vaudreuil	**5b**
Rivière-du-Loup	**4a**	Sainte-Dorothée	**5a**	Verchères	**5b**
Roberval	**3a**	Sainte-Hyacinthe	**4b**	Victoriaville	**4b**
Saint-André-Avellin	**4a**	Sainte-Madeleine	**5a**	Warwick	**4b**
Saint-Étienne-de-Lauzon	**4b**	Sainte-Marie-de-Beauce	**4b**		

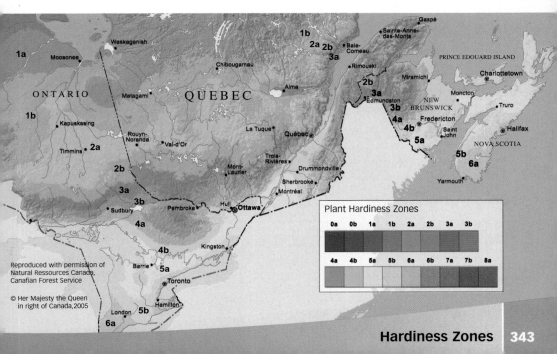

Plant Hardiness Zones

0a 0b 1a 1b 2a 2b 3a 3b

4a 4b 5a 5b 6a 6b 7a 7b 8a

Reproduced with permission of
Natural Ressources Canada,
Canafian Forest Service

© Her Majesty the Queen
in right of Canada,2005

Cut Flowers

Plus all grasses and roses…

Shrubs

Plus all hydrangeas and lilacs…

Native Canadian Plants

Plants for Moist Shade

Plants Tolerating Wet Conditions

Plus all aquatic plants…

* Hummingbirds

Plants with Evergreen Foliage

Plus most conifers...

Potentially Toxic Plants

Scented Plants

Plus most roses...

PASSION JARDINS

LOWER SAINT LAWRENCE

Centre-Jardin Montminy
82, route 132
La Pocatière, QC
G0R 1Z0
Tel.: (418) 856-2114

Embellissement Rivière-du-Loup (inc)
409 B, rue Témiscouata
Rivière-du-Loup, QC
G5R 6B3
Tel.:(418) 862-0203

Maurice Bélanger Paysagiste (inc)
175, chemin St-Benoît Est
Amqui, QC
G5J 2C2
Tel.: (418) 629-4673

QUEBEC CITY REGION

Aux Primeverts Centre Jardin
285, avenue St-Jacques
St-Raymond, QC
G3L 4A2
Tel.: (418) 337-7797

Ferme Bédard & Blouin
2157, boulevard Louis XIV
Québec, QC
G1C 1A1
Tel.: (418) 666-5518

CENTRAL QUEBEC

Jardinerie Fernand Fortier
99, route 116 Est
Princeville, QC
G6L 4K6
Tel.: (819) 364-5009

Pépinière L'Avenir
209, route 143
L'Avenir, QC
J0C 1B0
Tel.: (819) 394-2466

Les Serres Perreault
2, rue Beauchesne
Warwick, QC
J0A 1M0
Tel. : (819) 358-4419

Signé Garneau Paysagiste
29, boulevard Arthabaska est
Victoriaville, QC
G6P 6R9
Tel. : (819) 758-3887

CHAUDIÈRE-APPALACHES

Serres Laliberté
428, chemin de la Rivière-Etchemin
Ste-Claire, QC
G0R 2V0
Tel. : (418) 883-3998

Les Embellissements La Chaudière
1050, boulevard Vachon Sud
Ste-Marie de Beauce, QC
G6E 2S5
Tel.: (418) 387-2721

Ferme Horticole Lajoie
330, boulevard St-Vallier,
Route 132
St-Vallier, QC
G0R 4J0
Tel. : (418) 884-3124

Jardinerie Pousce-Vert
494, rue Principale
St-Étienne de Lauzon, QC
G6J 1G5
Tel.: (418) 831-5005

EASTERN TOWNSHIPS

Paysagistes Hollande
95, route 141
Ayer's Cliff, QC
J0B 1C0
Tel.: (819) 838-4906

Serres et Pépinière St-Élie
4675, boulevard Industriel
Sherbrooke, QC
J1L 2W5
Tel.: (819) 564-3243

Jardins Foster
749, rue Lakeside
Lac Brome, QC
J0E 1R0
Tel.: (450) 539-3869

LANAUDIÈRE

Jardinière du Nord
1000, chemin Joliette
St-Félix-de-Valois, QC
J0K 2M0
Tel.: (450) 889-4566

Complexe Horticole Bastien
4835, chemin Martin
Terrebonne, QC
J6X 4H4
Tel.: (450) 477-1919

Pépinière Villeneuve
951, rang de la Presqu'Île
L'Assomption, QC
J5W 3P4
Tel.: 1-888-589-7158

LAURENTIANS

Les Serres Arundel
37, chemin du Village
C.P. 98
Arundel, QC J0T 1A0
Tel.: (819) 687-3254

LAVAL

Pépinière R.Y. Locas
3254, boulevard Ste-Rose
Laval, QC
H7P 4K8
Tel.: (450) 622-0347

Charbonneau L'Expert
6, boulevard Samson
Ste-Dorothée , Laval, QC
H7X 3Y3
Tel.: (450) 689-1934

MAURICIE

Gauthier Fleurs & Jardins
4936, boulevard
Gene-H-Kruger
Trois-Rivières, QC
G9A 4N1
Tel.: (819) 375-4813

MONTEREGIAN AREA

Pépinière Jacques-Cartier 84
925, Jacques-Cartier sud
St-Jean-sur-Richelieu, QC
J3B 6Y8
Tel.: (450) 347-2242

Serres et Jardins Girouard
355, St-Simon, C.P. 107
Ste-Madeleine, QC
J0H 1S0
Tel.: (450) 795-3309

Centre de jardin M. Labonté
168, rue Calixa-Lavallée
Verchères, QC
J0L 2R0
Tel.: (450) 583-6626

Centre du Jardin Vaudreuil-sur-le-Lac
999, avenue St-Charles
Vaudreuil-Dorion, QC
J7V 8P5
Tel.: (450) 424-0844

Groupe Scardera

1887, chemin du Tremblay
Longueuil, QC
J4N 1A4
Tel.: (450) 468-0950

MONTREAL

Pépinière Pauls (1986)
9519, boulevard Gouin Ouest
Pierrefonds, QC
H8Y 1T7
Tel.: (514) 684-0297

OUTAOUAIS REGION

Rossignol des Prés
453, Sainte-Julie Est
St-André Avellin, QC
J0V 1W0
Tel.: (819) 983-2886

Emery plus qu'un centre jardin
600. boulevard
Maloney Est
Gatineau, QC
J8P 7M4
Tel.: (819) 663-1331

NEW BRUNSWICK

Serres chez Eugène
45, rue de la Tourbe
Lamèque,
Nouveau Brunswick
E8T 1A4
Tel.: (506) 344-7878

ONTARIO

Les Serres Legault
1810, Route 34
Hawkesbury, ONT
K6A 2R2
Tel.: (613) 632-1177